WE'MOON '93

INVOKING SPIRIT

GAIA RHYTHMS: AN ASTROLOGICAL MOON
CALENDAR, APPOINTMENT BOOK, AND DAILY
GUIDE TO NATURAL RHYTHM FOR WEMOON

WE'MOON '93: GAIA RHYTHMS for WOMYN

© Mother Tongue Ink 1992
Musawa, Editor & Publisher/Distributor
37010 SE Snuffin Rd.
Estacada, Oregon 97023
USA (tel. 503-630-7848)

© Hana Amazon

Distributed directly by the publisher,
or by the following fine distributors:

USA

Armadillo
5795 W. Washington Blvd.
Culver City, CA 90232

Bookpeople
2929 Fifth St.
Berkeley, CA 94710

Calyx
PO Box B
Corvallis, OR 97339-0539

Inland Book Company
PO Box 261
East Haven, CT 06512

Moving Books, Inc.
PO Box 20037
Seattle, WA 98102

New Leaf Distributing Co.
5425 Tulane Drive S.W.
Atlanta, GA 30336-2323

Small Changes
P.O. Box 19046
Seattle, WA 98109

VisionWorks
16 Chapman Street
Greenfield, MA 01301

International

Airlift Book Company
26/28 Eden Grove
London N78EL
England

Bookpeople
2929 Fifth St.
Berkeley, CA 94710 USA

Frauenliteraturvertrieb
Enrich-Ollenhauer-Strasse 231
D-6200 Wiesbaden
West Germany

Individuals can order this book directly from publisher @ $13.00 plus $2.00 postage and handling. When ordering 3 or more sent to the SAME ADDRESS, there is no charge for postage and handling.
Price: $13   ISBN 0-9510661-45   printed on recycled paper with soy ink

Table of Contents

INTRODUCTION by Musawa (and others as credited)

© Osha

MOON CALENDAR

Features:

Herbs by Colette Gardiner

Astrological predictions by Gretchen Lawlor

13 Moons: (begins on page 28)

I. Earth Mother Moon	VIII. Celebration Moon
II. Moon of Visions	IX. Everyday Magic Moon
III. Dreaming Moon	X. Meditation Moon
IV. Earth Loving Moon	XI. Shape-Shifting Moon
V. Prayer Moon	XII. Oracle Moon
VI. Moon of Muses	XIII. Elementals Moon
VII. Moon of Flow	

APPENDIX

Monthly lunar calendars
Planetary ephemeris
Why Asteroids?
Asteroid ephemeris
Acknowledgments
Contributor by-lines
Invitation to contribute; upcoming themes

© Angela Von Lintel Lobitz 1991

1993

JANUARY

S	M	T	W	T	F	S
					1	2
3	4	5	6	7	8	9
10	11	12	13	14	15	16
17	18	19	20	21	22	23
24	25	26	27	28	29	30
31						

FEBRUARY

S	M	T	W	T	F	S
	1	2	3	4	5	6
7	8	9	10	11	12	13
14	15	16	17	18	19	20
21	22	23	24	25	26	27
28						

MARCH

S	M	T	W	T	F	S
	1	2	3	4	5	6
7	8	9	10	11	12	13
14	15	16	17	18	19	20
21	22	23	24	25	26	27
28	29	30	31			

APRIL

S	M	T	W	T	F	S
				1	2	3
4	5	6	7	8	9	10
11	12	13	14	15	16	17
18	19	20	21	22	23	24
25	26	27	28	29	30	

MAY

S	M	T	W	T	F	S
						1
2	3	4	5	6	7	8
9	10	11	12	13	14	15
16	17	18	19	20	21	22
23	24	25	26	27	28	29
30	31					

JUNE

S	M	T	W	T	F	S
		1	2	3	4	5
6	7	8	9	10	11	12
13	14	15	16	17	18	19
20	21	22	23	24	25	26
27	28	29	30			

JULY

S	M	T	W	T	F	S
				1	2	3
4	5	6	7	8	9	10
11	12	13	14	15	16	17
18	19	20	21	22	23	24
25	26	27	28	29	30	31

AUGUST

S	M	T	W	T	F	S
1	2	3	4	5	6	7
8	9	10	11	12	13	14
15	16	17	18	19	20	21
22	23	24	25	26	27	28
29	30	31				

SEPTEMBER

S	M	T	W	T	F	S
			1	2	3	4
5	6	7	8	9	10	11
12	13	14	15	16	17	18
19	20	21	22	23	24	25
26	27	28	29	30		

OCTOBER

S	M	T	W	T	F	S
					1	2
3	4	5	6	7	8	9
10	11	12	13	14	15	16
17	18	19	20	21	22	23
24	25	26	27	28	29	30
31						

NOVEMBER

S	M	T	W	T	F	S
	1	2	3	4	5	6
7	8	9	10	11	12	13
14	15	16	17	18	19	20
21	22	23	24	25	26	27
28	29	30				

DECEMBER

S	M	T	W	T	F	S
			1	2	3	4
5	6	7	8	9	10	11
12	13	14	15	16	17	18
19	20	21	22	23	24	25
26	27	28	29	30	31	

What is WE'MOON?

The **We'Moon: Gaia Rhythms for Womyn** is more than an appointment book. It is about getting in touch with our own true nature. **We'Moon** is a *handbook in natural rhythm*. We chart our days alongside other heavenly bodies, and discover patterns in how we inter-relate. **We'Moon** comes out of an *international womyn's culture*. Art and writings by wemoon from many lands give a glimpse of the great diversity and uniqueness of a world we create in our own image. **We'Moon** is about *womyn's spirituality* (spirit'reality). We share how we live our truth, what we are inspired by, how we envision our reality in connection with the whole earth and all our relations.

We'Moon means "We of the Moon". The moon, whose cycles run in our blood, was the original womyn's calendar. Like the moon, wemoon circle the earth. We are drawn to one another. We come in different shapes, colors and sizes. We are continually transforming. With all our different hues and points of view, we are one.

We'Moon means wemoon. Instead of defining ourselves in relation to men, ("Woman" means "wife of man" in old English; "female" is another derivative from "male"), we use the word *wemoon* to define ourselves by our primary relation to the natural sources of cosmic flow ("We of the moon"). Other terms commonly used among wemoon are: *womyn, wimmin, womon, womb-one.* **We'Moon** is a moon calendar for wemoon. As wemoon, whole in ourselves, we do not need "the other half" to complete the picture. In **We'Moon** we see the whole range of life's potential embodied by wemoon. We also do not divide the rest of the universe into sex-role stereotypes according to the heterosexual model. We see the goddess equally in the sun and the moon, in the earth and the sky.

We'Moon is global. The **We'Moon Almanac** originated on womyn's lands in Europe and was published in different countries and different languages through most of the '80's, until settling down on We'Moon Healing Ground in Oregon (USA), where it is now produced. Though it was transplanted many times, **We'Moon** always has been rooted in the living earth, tended by lesbians on land, and grown out of a global culture of wemoon creating. The alternating languages for the days of the week and months on the calendar pages are what is left of its multilingual origins.

We'Moon culture exists in the diversity and oneness of our experience as wemoon. Wemoon are in all cultures, coming from very different ways of life, and wemoon have a culture of our own, sharing a common mother root. Unfortunately, both our differences and our unity are threatened by (i.e. threatening to) the patriarchal need to claim all as their own. Consequently, we sometimes have conflicting priorities. On the one hand, we need to preserve the positive parts of our cultures of origin. This is especially true for indigenous wemoon from endangered earth-loving cultures. On the other 5 hand, we also need to break free from traditional ways that keep us from our power as wemoon. This is especially so in dominant cultures where the patriarchal overlay is the heaviest. In **We'Moon**, we invite every wemoon to share how the "Mother Tongue" speaks to her, with respect for both cultural integrity and individual freedom.

Mother Tongue Ink is the name Musawa has published the We'Moon under, over the years. The "Mother Tongue" is our native language—every culture has its own; it is the language we learn from our mothers. The "Mother Tongue" is also universal: it is the language Mother Nature speaks to all. We can hear her in the wind, in the music of the spheres, in our inner way of knowing, feeling and sensing. **We'Moon** is published in the many languages of wemoon's experience, with lots of pictures, natural cycles, international signs and symbols, and calendar pages in different languages. As **We'Moon** grows and changes, so will the languages we share. **We'Moon '93** is also available with German translation (by Labyrinthverlag, Braunschweig) and on audiotape (by Hikane). We invite your translations into other Mother Tongues for the days and months in next year's calendar pages.

Bouddyke

6

Introduction to the Theme: INVOKING SPIRIT

Invocation literally means "calling in". This **We'Moon** is about calling the power of Spirit into our lives. When I was young, I once asked an older black woman what praying was. I came from a non-religious, humanistically inclined family, and I was really curious what people did when they believed in God. I always remembered her answer—and my immediate response. She said, "Praying is doing something beautiful for God". I responded by raising my arms from my sides up around my head and back down again, three times (because that was my lucky number). Now I recognize that stance in the Nile River Goddess on our front cover. She is not standing in a static pose (unlikely for a river goddess), she is actively reaching out engaging the world of spirit, at one with the flow.

Somehow the child in me already knew this most ancient of invocation postures, standing rooted in the earth, raising energy in my little body with full wing span outstretched, gathering in through my crown chakra, giving out through my heart. It remained my secret ritual of devotion to this day—always in nature, alone, at special moments, from me to the universe. As children, we naturally know something about spirit being alive in us, in our bodies and in our very real connection with the earth—not just something above and beyond or outside of ourselves. Our grown wemoon bodies do not forget this, as expressed in the painting, "Moon Time," on our back cover. Ancient and new, reaching up or squatting down, snake and bird goddess or contemporary wemoon...our power to invoke spirit is in the current of life energy coming through. This **We'Moon** is dedicated to the inner Goddess in all, waiting inside for us to bring Her out, reaching out in us to connect with all there is, calling out in beauty, calling in Spirit.

What are the ways we connect with Spirit in our lives? This is the theme for **We'Moon '93**. Spirit is always present; but we are not. Becoming present, turning inward, allowing awareness, being inspired, getting the spirit...whatever the words used, it comes through experience in the present moment in relation to the wholeness of being. How do you invoke Presence? What is your magic? How do you go between the worlds? These are the kinds of questions we asked of wemoon in our "Call for Contributions." Each of the 13 Moons explores a different pathway to Spirit, as offered by We'Moon contributors on this theme.

© *Megan Wilson*

In creating We'Moon this year, we committed ourselves to take the theme to heart, from the beginning, and invoke the presence of spirit in all our work. Elaborate rituals at first gave way to simpler forms as we went along: making an altar or smudging the space we worked in, singing together or taking a walk under the moon. We took time for feelings and to remember to bring our bodies along, to keep touching the earth and celebrating the cycles.

In the first circle we did to create the "Call for Contributions," we visualized our We'Moon circle within the circle of this we'moon land and the whole earth. Our roots connecting with the center, we felt our connection with all beings in spirit, circles within circles, spiraling out to wemoon who wished to hear this Call and respond. We envisioned Spider Woman spinning Her web, gathering in the treasures of wemoon creating, and beyond to the wemoon who would read this **We'Moon** and respond. We discovered that we were not putting this "Call" out by ourselves. We heard the urgency of Mother Earth, Herself, calling out for wemoon, especially, to connect with Spirit in and around us, that we may heal into wholeness and mend the web of life. May the Moon paths we travel together this year empower us to do that.

Creating this We'Moon together also taught us that invoking spirit is just the beginning. Bringing spirit into form and staying with it through the trials and tribulations of the mater-real world is the hardest part of wemoon's work...and it is never done! In one of our later circles, we created a spiral of 13 stones (for the Moons) within a circle of 12 stones (for the signs) on the deck in front of my little house in the woods to help concentrate the energy needed for the last phase of bringing the spirit of **We'Moon** into form. On the very day I was finishing up this Introduction, an iridescent blue/green peacock (as big as the deck) with goddess eyes all over landed out of no where right on the spiral...as if to say: and it is so! It is now in our hands. Pass it on. Blessed Be.   musawa

Pupurangi II   ©*Minerva 1991*

8

We'Moon Primer: How to Use This Book

Ancient people have always looked to the sky to discover patterns in our way of moving here on earth. They assumed naturally a connection with a larger whole of which we are each one small part.

The **We'Moon** follows this same basic structure, showing the natural cycles of moon, sun, planets and stars as they relate to earth. By recording our own activities, side by side with those of other heavenly bodies, we get a chance to notice what connection, if any, there is for us.

As seen from earth, the moon and the sun are equal in size: "the left and right eyes of Heaven," according to Eastern astrology. Unlike the solar dominated calendars of white Western patriarchy, in **We'Moon** we look at our experience through both eyes at once.

The moon goes around the earth thirteen times, while the earth goes around the sun once. As a **lunar calendar**, *days* are marked by the phases of the moon, *months* begin with the new moon, and *thirteen Moons/Months* are given (with two pages of we'moon graphics and writings in between), for the number of complete revolutions of the moon in a lunar year. The **solar** counterpoint is observed as the turning points in the sun cycle (Solstices and Equinoxes, with the lunar/solar Cross-Quarter days in between). This is the natural basis for the seasonal celebrations that vary in name, time and place from culture to culture. In the Southern Hemisphere the sun season is always opposite the Northern Hemisphere, just as night and day are opposite in East and West, affirming the power of dark and light giving birth to each other. This year's **We'Moon** begins on the **Full Moon** just before Winter Solstice (the last half of the 13th Moon of 1991), and ends with the Full Moon after Solstice, in 1993.

Astrology gives a third way to measure the cycles, relating the sun, the moon, and all other planets in our universe through the star signs. *The moon passes through all twelve signs of the zodiac each month, while the sun goes through only one sign a month, for twelve months.* The other planets that revolve around the sun with earth, have different cycles, also measured by their movements through the zodiac. Imagine a clock (with many hands...): the earth is the center, from which we view our universe; all other planets are like the hands with different rates of movement; and the twelve star signs of the zodiac are like the numbers that mark the movement we see in time and space. The positions of the planets (where they are each day in the thirty degrees of each star sign), are given in the monthly ephemeris tables in back - and the patterns they make in relation to each other are given in the aspects (noted under the date each day).

The lunar and solar cycles are like two hands drumming, each playing a different beat. As the earth dances with them, she tilts, she lilts, rhythmically changing the intensity, the color, the light or heat. Then the stars give the time signature—syncopated moon rhythm over slow bass beat of the sun. All other planets in our solar system chime in with their own tones in their own times.

The astrological signs are the tunes that the planets intone. And all forms of life on this planet are the instruments through which the music of the spheres is played out. As we begin to feel the rhythm, hear the tones and experience the harmony in our every day lives, we can begin to play with it. When we become conscious of our parts in the whole piece, we start to be able to shape the instruments of our own lives, to choose the sounds we wish to make, and to sing from our hearts the harmonies we resonate most deeply with, until all of earth life is one song.

© Sudie Rakusin 1986

Astrological Moon Calendar

Signs: The 12 signs of the zodiac are a kind of mandala in the sky, marking off 30° segments in the 360° circle around the earth. As the Moon and Sun progress around the zodiac, the symbols are written in on the calendar to highlight when they enter a new sign. This gives an indication of major shifts in planetary energy that affect life on earth in the grand matrix of interaction with our closest relations in the sky. These sign changes (e.g. ☽→♈) are also listed along with all the planets in the aspects given for each day.

Moon sign: The moon sign is written in beside the Moon phase every day. The moon changes signs approximately every 2 1/2 days, going through all twelve signs of the zodiac every 28 days (the sidereal month). The moon sign reflects qualities of your inner core self. See "Moon Signs/Moon Transits".

Sun Sign: The sun enters a new sign once a month (around the 20th or so), completing the whole circle of the zodiac in one year. Your birthday indicates your sun sign - where the sun was on the day you were born - and celebrates the return of the sun to that point each year. The sun sign describes qualities of your visible personality, your outward shining self. See "Sun Signs".

Moon Void of Course: The time just before the moon changes sign can be disorienting unless you use it to ground and center yourself. The moon is Void of Course from the time of the last significant lunar aspect (marked v/c next to that time in the aspects) until the moon enters a new sign.

Eclipses occur only at new moon (solar eclipses) or full moon (lunar eclipses), when the earth and moon orbits intersect such that one blocks the light of the other. The time it occurs is approximately the same time as given for the new or full moon). The letter in parenthesis indicates the <u>type</u> of eclipse it is (T=total; P=partial; A=annular).

AP/PG: Apogee(Ap) is the point in the orbit of a planet or the moon that is farthest from earth. The effects of transits at this time may be less noticeable immediately, but may appear later on. A good time to plant root crops. **Perigee(Pg)** is the point in the orbit of a planet or the moon that is nearest to earth. Transits with the moon or other planets when they are **Pg** will be more intense. A good time to plant above-ground crops.

What signs are the planets in? When planets enter a new sign, this is indicated with a little arrow (e.g., $4 \rightarrow \nearrow$). Planets are like chakras in our solar system allowing for different frequencies or types of energy to be expressed.

Retrograde or Direct: The times when a planet goes Retrograde (℞) or Direct (D) are also marked with the aspects. This indicates whether the planets are moving backward or forward through the signs of the zodiac...(an optical illusion, much like being on a moving train passing a slower train, which appears to be going backward). In direct motion, planetary energies are more straightforward; in retrograde, planetary energies turn back in on themselves, are more involuted.

For those more astrologically inclined: the exact positions of all planets are given in the Ephemeris, opposite the Month Calendars. The ephemeris shows where each planet is every day at Noon, GMT (international time). The aspects (the angle of relation between planets in the sky) are given each day underneath the date. Aspects are given in PST (Pacific Standard Time before April 4 and after October 31); and PDT (Pacific Daylight Savings Time) between those dates in April and October.

ALL STATED TIMES IN THIS CALENDAR ARE GIVEN IN PST / PDT (PACIFIC STANDARD OR DAYLIGHT TIME) UNLESS OTHER-WISE STATED. At the bottom of each page EST / EDT (Eastern Standard or Daylight Time) and GMT (Greenwich Mean Time) are also given. The World Time Zones map and chart show how to convert these times from the West Coast time (USA) to your local time.

Holidays / Holy Days

Only the natural holidays, in the yearly dance of the earth-moon-sun cycle are given in this **We'Moon.** *If you do not find the holidays of your particular spiritual/cultural tradition, do not feel left out!* They most likely fall around the turning points in the earth-moon-sun cycle as given. Only the names, exact dates, and specific events to be celebrated have been changed through the ages according to the prevailing culture. There are still cultures today (such as Hindu, Jewsh, Muslim and Buddhist), that honor the lunar cycles by celebrating many holidays on new and full moons. At the root of all people's cultures - if you dig far enough - is a reverence for Mother Earth and a celebration of the natural cycles throughout the seasons of Earth's passage in relation to her closest relatives in the universe.

Goddess of the Wheel of the Year ✪ *Sheila Broun*　　12

The Wheel of the Year

The seasonal cycle of the year is created by the relationship of the earth to the sun and moon - the interplay of night and day, dark and light, receptivity and activity. Winter Solstice marks the North point on the wheel, when the nights are longest. It is the most reflective, yin time of year. Summer Solstice at the South point of the wheel marks the time of the longest day of the year, the most active, yang season.

Thus, strong polarities on the wheel are the Solstices, while the Equinoxes mark the midpoints in the energy shift from one pole to another. Spring Equinox, the East point on the wheel, and Fall Equinox, the West point on the wheel, are the times when the lengths of day and night are at a balance point.

Located between the Solstices and the Equinoxes are the Lunar Cross-Quarter Days. The traditional dates given in the calendar are the mid-points of each season, when the subtle shifts in the energy - such as the balance of light and dark - become visible in nature. For example, the renewal of the sun at Winter Solstice begins to be noticed by Candlemas as the days get longer. (Remember: the Northern and Southern Hemispheres experience the seasons in a mirror image: when it is Candlemas in the North, it is Lammas in the south).

While cross-quarter days are important holidays in the Solar Wheel of the Year, marking shifts in the earth-sun relationship, they are primarily *lunar holidays*. Wemoon may wish to celebrate them on the appropriate new or full moon, according to the season in the calendar as *lunar cross quarter days*).

Traditionally, Beltane (May Day) and Lammas (Harvest Moon) are full moon festivals at which fertile, abundant creative energy is celebrated, the time of ovulation and conception in we'moon cycles. Samhain (Hallowmas) and Imbolc (Candlemas) are traditionally the dark moon festivals, when death and rebirth, the crone, the underworld journey is celebrated, the time in tribal cultures when wemoon bleed together.

The sun's cycle of a year mirrors the moon's monthly cycle: Winter Solstice is like the dark or new moon, Spring Equinox is like the waxing half moon, Summer Solstice is like the full moon, and Fall Equinox is like the waning half moon. In the Wheel of the Year, this counter -point between sun and moon is celebrated, in the turning of the seasons on earth, with the alternating solar and lunar festivals.

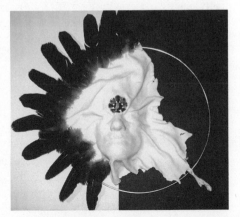

Embracing Diversity © *Susan Jansen*

The Planetary Dance 1993

Many prophecies have been made about great earth changes to occur in the 90's. Planetary configurations support this sense of monumental changes. One such configuration is the rare and potent union of Uranus and Neptune in Capricorn, which has been influencing us for several years as these two move slowly into an exact conjunction. They become a single point of light three times in 1993; on February 2, August 19 and October 25, always at 18-19 degrees of Capricorn. Not only do these two conjunct only every 180 years, but it's happening in an already tense and complex celestial situation we have been experiencing since the late 1980's.

Whenever Uranus, Neptune and Pluto are active, the collective consciousness is stressed. The inner sea, the ocean of the unconscious is heaving in a storm of terrific proportions. The collective unconscious is erupting into our conscious minds. Imagination, inspiration and a glimpse of the divine all intrude into our most ordinary daily thoughts.

A major shift is happening within us now. Capricorn represents the foundation stones upon which we base our understanding of life. Uranus and Neptune are planets of dissolution and change, not easily compatible and yet dominating the picture with their tight, intense union. A reality which we have taken for granted for a long time and which holds absolute authority over us is blowing apart. Uranus, Neptune, Pluto in Scorpio, and Saturn in Aquarius combine to create a unique doorway, a "mind change" where consciousness and reality break open and then reform in a completely new way. Dissolution and disintegration of the old, then sudden reintegration around a new set of values and goals characterized by a quality of inclusiveness.

The inner world mirrors the outer. Neptune in an earth sign: the earth is becoming more sensitive, susceptible, permeable. Uranus in an earth sign: the earth is rebelling, overreacting, in chaos, searching for her own rights and individuality. External issues call up our inner responses, mirror our inner processes. Boundaries between ourselves and the rest of the world are being softened; circumstances are less predictable, and we are more vulnerable to impressions from our larger, world community. What happens anywhere on the earth impacts us as it never has before. We are being forced to become a global society.   © *Gretchen Lawlor 1992*

Significant aspects

☌   Conjunct (0-5°): linked together, mutually enhancing
∗   Sextile (60°): 2 signs apart, cooperative
☐   Square (90°): 3 signs apart, challenging
△   Trine (120°): 4 signs apart, harmonizing
☍   Opposition (180°): 6 signs apart, complementing or polarizing

14

Planets

Goddesses *

(1) Personal Skills

☿   *Mercury:* communication; inventiveness

     Metis, goddess of counsel; wisdom.

♀   *Venus:* relationship, empathy

     Aphrodite, goddess of grace and love.

♂   *Mars:* assertiveness, ambition

     Dione, goddess of sexuality, growth, struggle

(2) Social Involvements

♃   *Jupiter:* opportunities, leadership

     Themis, goddess of time, justice, prophecy

♄   *Saturn:* discipline, limitation

     Rhea, goddess of natural order and peace

(3) Collective, Generational Issues

♅   *Uranus:* revolutions, radical changes

     Urania, goddess of heaven and earth

♆   *Neptune:* spiritual awakenings

     Tethys, goddess of seas and oceans

♇   *Pluto:* death/rebirth of self-image, lifestyle

     Persephone, goddess of death in life, life in death

* from Matriarchal Zodiac © Blue Moonfire 1985

Sun Signs

MESHA – GOAT

Aries - Spark   ♈   Cardinal /Fire
Born March 21-April 19. Aries approaches life with the exploratory innocence of the newborn. Eager and excited she leaps before she looks. "Here I am, I exist" she cries joyfully setting out on a path of discovery.

VRISHABA – BULL

Taurus - Rock   ♉   Fixed/Earth
Born April 20-May 20. Taurus is grounded in the sensual pleasure of physical existence. Like a rock she is warmed by the sun and cooled by the rain, giving back the energy she receives in constant connectedness.

(continued on next page)   15

MITHUNA – LOVERS

KATAKA – CRAB

SIMHA – LION

KANYA – MAIDEN

THULA – SCALE

Sun Signs (continued)

Gemini - Breeze ♊ Mutable/Air
Born May 20-June 20. In knowing one thing Gemini has to explore its opposite. In the realm of ideas her mercurial mind speedily travels, building bridges of communication between polarities.

Cancer - Spring ♋ Cardinal/Water
Born June 21-July 21. Like one of her symbols the tortoise, Cancer carries her house with her and makes home wherever she finds herself. She is sensitive to all the beings living on her home planet Earth and provides nurturance like an ever flowing spring from deep within.

Leo - Flame ♌ Fixed/Fire
Born July 22 - August 21. The childlike sunny heart of Leo loves to dramatise life and show off all its glory. Her boundless energy pours out in generous loving creativity. She attracts others' attention and her inspiring qualities make her a natural leader.

Virgo - Soil ♍ Mutable/Earth
Born August 22 - September 21: Virgo is the sign of wholeness and healing. The dualisms of body/mind, sexuality/spirituality are unified in her fertile soil. Virgo knows the secret of creation grounded in the Earth and pays attention to the details of manifestation.

Libra - Breath ♎ Cardinal/Air
Born September 22 - October 22. Breathing in and out harmoniously in tune with cosmic law is the essence of Libra. She strives for perfect balance, truth and justice. Libra, of all the signs, understands the need to work co-operatively. 16

Sun Signs (continued)

Scorpio - Geyser ♏ Fixed/Water

Born October 23 - November 19. Scorpio goes into the Underworld of the psyche to explore the deep mysteries of birth, sexuality and death. Knowing power she can receive a gift from the most terrifying monster.

Sagittarius - Wild Fire ♐ Mutable/Fire

Born November 20 - December 20. Sagittarius the wild horse, likes open spaces to gallop in. She loves to travel, share her experiences and seek truth. In touch with the divine in the natural world, she instinctively worships the Universe.

Capricorn - Mountain ♑ Cardinal/Earth

Born December 21-January 18. Capricorn's approach to life is mature, practical and sensual. She climbs the mountain not to conquer it but for the experience. Living on the frontiers of possibility and loving to build, Capricorn is at the foundations of civilization.

Aquarius - Airwaves ♒ Fixed/Air

Born January 19 - February 17. Aquarius is a sign of paradox and apparent opposites: group unity/individual freedom, science/intuition, rebellion/rigidity, impatience/fascination with structures - which gives her a broad overview on life and the talent of a futuristic visionary.

Pisces - Ocean ♓ Mutable/Water

Born February 18-March 19. Embryo Pisces swims like a fish in the womb of the Universe. Pulled by the currents surrounding her and influenced by Neptune's dreams and intuition, she manifests strongly prophetic visionary powers.

Drawings by Minerva, astrology by Gretchen Lawlor & Osha One. © Creative Cronies, Moon Calendar Productions 1990, New Zealand

17

Moon Signs / Moon Transits

Your moon sign reflects your innermost being—your emotional, psychic, intuitional, creative deep self-rather than your will or ego identity as with the sun sign. The moon moves through the signs of the zodiac once a month in the same order as the sun does. We have regrouped the moon transits here according to the elements associated with each sign. Elemental Power!

The Creative Elements The signs of the zodiac express the vital creative energies of the four elements-fire, earth, air and water. There are three signs which distribute the qualities of each element. Use the elemental flow of each moon sign to co-create your works of life and art.

FIRE MOONS Our creativity is stimulated with exuberant warmth, spontaneity and leaps of faith during fire moons. Physical energy is high and spirited activities find outlets. These are good times for athletics, dance, martial arts, performance and romantic enjoyments.

ARIES, The Promising Moon. Aries initiates activities and urges self-assertion. Restlessness and discontent fuel exploration, fresh approaches and discoveries. We are quick to express feelings, attitudes and desires. This vividly appreciative energy is nice for design and color work.
*When **dark**: awaken adventure; When **full**: quests quicken.*

LEO, The Performing Moon. Leo generates feelings of being special. Generous warmth and vitality come easily. Romantic interludes and creative outbursts are possible. This childlike and extroverted energy enhances all aspects of theatre work, broadcasting, movement and dance. Exhibiting, costumes and adornments are all highlighted.
*When **dark**: ardent arousal; When **full**: rave reviews.*

SAGITTARIUS, The Teaching Moon. During sagittarius free expression is energized. Opinions are valued and tongues are swift and sure. Teaching and promotional activities come easily. Our gregariousness can feed gatherings of all kinds. Sagittarius stimulates a love of learning and movement. Exercise your freedom to travel.
*When **dark**: feed beliefs; When **full**: wise aspirations.*

EARTH MOONS We create with the substances and material of the Earth Herself during earth moons. These signs are the providers who nurture the practical grounding of our work. Sensual expression and a regard for useful purpose are highlighted. We can access greater physical endurance now. These are good times for gardening, working with clay, glass, wood and metal. 18

CAPRICORN, The Building Moon. We can solidify our intentions in the material world during capricorn. Ambition, work, diligence and duty combine with strength of will and commitment to purpose. The slow, step by step processes using natural materials can be applied now.
*When **dark**: ambitions arise; When **full**: assume importance.*

TAURUS, The Sensuous Moon. Appreciative taurus energy loves the physical plane. This is a good time to beautify surroundings and acquire belongings. Intuitive touch can inspire works of art, massage or lovemaking. Tend to bodily needs and pleasures now. Music and song are taurean enhancements that embellish our lives.
*When **dark**: truly touching; When **full**: behold the bold.*

VIRGO, The Healing Moon. It's time for self-improvement when the moon channels virgo. Preciseness of intent and mental dexterity can be accessed now. Allow the attention to detail and organizational abilities of virgo to shore up projects. Assess health care needs and dietary habits now. Crafts, repetitive designs and collections are favorable expressions of virgo.
*When **dark**: organize priorities; When **full**: adjust attitudes.*

AIR MOONS Changeable air moons stimulate communicative insights that help us create through writing, conversation, recording, photography and musical instruments. Air energy is favorable for being in the moment and allowing ideas, improvisation and witty relatedness to surface. Study, social gathering, singing, networking and media work are all highlighted during air time.

LIBRA, The Artistic Moon. Venus-ruled libra is a mentor of the arts. Beauty, balance, harmony, cooperation and poetic flow are her gifts. A good performing and social gathering time. Enjoy galleries and museums. Both friendly attractions and love connections can be delightful.
*When **dark**: balance bonds; When **full**: entertain allies.*

AQUARIUS, The Visionary Moon. This can be an unconventional and offbeat time when unique outpourings, spontaneity and innovation flow more easily. We can be seers of future times as our vision and insight get catalyzed in aquarius. This is a good gathering time for brainstorming and community exchange.
*When **dark**: remember the future; When **full**: revolutionary rewards.*

GEMINI, The Smiling Moon. The verbal possibilities for witty exchanges expand during playful gemini. These are good times for reading, writing, scripting, theatre, improvisation, comedy, meetings, potlucks and parties. Restlessness may fuel short trips, explorations, family visits and fun times.
*When **dark**: catalyze concepts; When **full**: mutable solutions.*   19

The Guardians of the Four Elements   © *Eva-Gesine Wegner*

WATER MOONS The creative flow of feeling and sensitivity rises to the surface during water moons. Meditation and retreat help poetics, journaling, listening, emotional sharing and musical or mystical flights of imagination. Ebbing into our memory-filled past can bring up moods and old patterns. When not seeking solitude, we may feel the urge to merge into heart and spirit space. A walk near water or a long bath can be healing during this time.

CANCER, The Mothering Moon. Both vulnerability and strength surface with our cancerian love for inclusive nurturance. Fertility of body and spirit feeds our inclinations towards home, family and our places of power within. Creative folk and culinary arts may be enjoyed. Gardening and planting have fruitful results now.
*When **dark**: hold your own; When **full**: fruition's feast.*

SCORPIO, The Witching Moon. Our natural inclinations to explore the mysteries surface during scorpio. Masks come on or off as passions well up. Intimacy and personal disclosures may be intense, while raw honesty may be confrontive. Private space assists our deep reflection. This is a good time for intuitive arts, rituals and divination.
*When **dark**: mystical messages; When **full**: tales of power.*

PISCES, The Poetic Moon. Our emotions and feelings are the creative elements during pisces. Unconscious motivations and old hurts may influence our moods. Seeking solitude to recharge our inner batteries may also enhance our intuitive imagination and dreamtime. Music can heighten our spirits.
*When **dark**: sensitive proximities; When **full**: empowering empathy.*

Lunar Rhythm: "we are the ebb, and we are the flow..."

The moon has a special power for women; we of the moon, wemoon! Her cycles run in our blood. She embodies the deep soul watery wicca flow of wemoon experience. She makes the invisible visible with her light that softens rather than sharpens differences and lets other lights shine with her. We see ourselves more clearly in her light. We know the whole is greater than the difference between the parts. We are not afraid of changes or differences - like the many faces of the moon, we are one.

Everything that flows moves in rhythm with the moon. She rules the water element on earth: the ocean's tides, the life fluids in plants/animals/people, underground currents in earth energy, and the moods of human mind, body behavior and emotion. Being the closest heavenly body to earth, it is the moon's presence that exerts the strongest pull...and all that moves is effected by this most intimate attraction. As the moon goes around all sides of the earth in one month, she slowly pulls a white veil of sunlight across her dark face. The **phase** and **sign** of the moon are indicators of which way she moves us. Where was the moon when you were born? She gives a sense of how you define yourself, of how you relate to where you are coming from and going toward in this life.

The Norns / Matronae/ Triple Mothers
© *Monica Sjoo 1990*

Moon Phases

New Moon: when the sun and the moon appear together in the earth's sky, the moon is invisible. The pull on us is most strong in one direction: both sun and moon are on the same side of the earth at the same time, they rise and set together and they are conjunct in the same sign of the zodiac. This is the fourth aspect of the "Triple Goddess": the mystery of endings and origins, a transition time, when the veil between worlds is thinnest. Time of inner spaces, heightened psychic powers, embryonic growth. Plant seeds with a blessing for new growth. <Knowing when the last new moon before your birth was (its sign and house position in your horoscope) helps define and give a sense of how you relate to your roots, Those born on or soon after the new moon are said to be "new souls adrift on life's seas. >*

Waxing Moon: the first crescent of the new moon (always facing left in the Northern Hemisphere, the opposite in the Southern Hemisphere) appears 2-3 nights after the dark of the moon, low in the Western sky. She rises an hour later each afternoon, and sets an hour later each night. By half moon, she is visible from noon until midnight. For two weeks, the moon's light is increasing and energy is rising, tending to be more active, outgoing and expressive. At half moon, the moon and sun are square to each other - a challenging situation which may bring growth through struggle. Artemis, goddess of enchantment, is the crescent moon who helps awaken consciousness and feelings. A creative and expansive time full of vital energy - begin new projects.

Full Moon: It always rises when the sun is setting. Moon and sun are on opposite sides of the earth, in opposite signs of the zodiac. Two such strong energies pulling in opposite directions can make it difficult to integrate them at this time - a source of creative tension, or conflict, an upsetting overload. Selene, goddess of plenty, brings fulfillments in projects, feelings, maturity; culmination of this moon cycle, the celebrant, the lover, the mother: giving forth. Full moon stimulates ovulation. <The first full moon after your birth (its sign and house position in your horoscope) is a strong indicator of how you define your goals in life and how you go about accomplishing them. Those born on or soon after the full moon are said to be "old souls" who may have strong emotions and also a strong sense of purpose.>*

Waning Moon: The moon rises an hour later after sunset every night following the full moon...by half moon, she is visible all morning, setting at noon. At 90° angles to each other in the sky, half moon and the sun are again square to each other, a challenging aspect. The waning crescent (facing right in the northern Hemisphere, left in the Southern Hemisphere) brings the awareness inward. In whatever field you are growing: reap what you sow, weed and cut back, prepare the ground, clear the way. Contraction and concentration of energy. Hecate takes us into the dark depths, for transformation and renewal.

*Musawa, *with <lunar notes from Elisabeth Dietz Gauerke>*

© *Susanne Hare*

Lunar Charts: A Native American Perspective

Native Astrology: "Among other things, for many thousands of years, the art of reading the sky was lovingly taught by the elders to the younger generation. Because each old person knew different things, our elders were like a living library...We believe knowledge should not stagnate on a shelf, but be lovingly poured from one generation to another. Many libraries have burned and books we never dreamed of were destroyed in ages past. But the things we needed to know survived by example. If all of our astrology books were removed tomorrow, how many of you could go outside and find the zodiac around your house?"

Know Your Moon: ...The real 'heart' of this book is the Moon: It is the closest heavenly body and seems to exert a tremendous physical and emotional influence on us all.

Of the 13 lunations a year, there are three considered very important... The first is, of course, one's natal moon's position. Then it is extremely important to consider the last new moon preceding the child's birth... The third most important moon is the first full moon after birth...

Lunar Charts: An interesting way to use the lunations and your moon's position is to do a lunar chart every month. It is just like a solar chart, except you use the moon and its degree to find the equal cusps. For example, if your moon is 10° Libra, you put 10° Libra on the ascendant, then put 10° Scorpio on the 2nd and 10° Sagittarius on the 3rd and so on. <u>Put your moon on the ascendant.</u> Then go right across the ephemeris for the current date and take planets except for the moon and insert them. Now add the new and full moon. If something special is planned - do the chart for that day. This will give you a true emotional barometer; a monthly emotional, personal forecast.

© *Elisabeth Dietz Gauerke 1989, excerpted with permission from* <u>The Medicine Road</u>.

Matriarchal Astrology...and Other Variations

There is some evidence that there were 13 signs in some ancient **matriarchal zodiacs**, corresponding to the 13 Moons of the lunar calendar (the 13th sign is thought to be "Arachne," the spider, in between Taurus and Gemini). Hindu astrology uses 28-30 **lunar houses** as well as the 12 solar houses associated with the zodiac as we know it, and views each person's chart through both "eyes of heaven" (the moon and the sun) at once. Other eras undoubtedly used other **numerology** in dividing the pie of the sky: Virgo and Scorpio, for instance were once merged together where Libra now is.

There are even two different versions of the zodiac based on the 12 star signs commonly used. The **Tropical Zodiac** uses the earth-sun cycle as its source, beginning with 0° Aries on the March Equinox; the **Sidereal Zodiac** uses the constellations' positions relative to earth as its source, which has drifted 29° backwards with the Procession of the Equinoxes (so the sun is said to be at 1° Pisces on the March Equinox). Like two clocks set to different time zones, both are valid. In this case, they seem to reflect different levels of reality. For example, when you plant by the ephemeris, using the Tropical Zodiac, you are encouraging growth in the vital physical-emotional energy fields; when you plant by the Sidereal Zodiac, you are speaking to the more subtle soul-spirit energies.

However you cut it, the sky encircles the earth, the planets move in cycles, and the signs describe a sequence of stages. . .in the movement of matter through space over time (eg., energy). The 12 signs we use now are only one way of looking at it - we'moon are all the time redefining the signs, and what they mean to us in the cycles of growth in our own lives.

In our currently **solar-dominated cultures**, when people ask: What is your sign? They generally mean your **Sun sign**. Remember that your **Moon sign** and **Rising sign** are just as important, and that every other planet has a sign in your natal chart as well. The qualities of the Zodiac Signs can be adapted to any planet, once you understand the kind of energy each planet channels in your life story.

Moon Nodes are another neglected part of we'moon astrology. They are the points of intersection where the orbits involving the sun, moon, and earth meet. They are about relationships in our family of origin, our inner circle, the alignment of our self-will and cosmic-will, and are linked with eclipses on the new and full moons. In your chart, the North (☊) and South (☋) Nodes point out the direction of your karma, the "head and tail of the dragon." Their positions are given in the ephemeris charts in back.

Asteroids: See"Why Asteroids?" & Asteroid Epehmeris in back.   24

World Time Zones

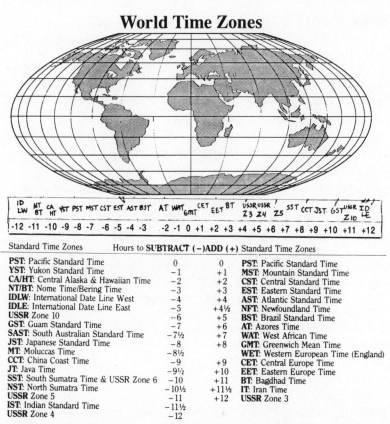

ID LW	NT BT	CA HT	YST	PST	MST	CST	EST	AST	BST	AT	WAT GMT	CET	EET	BT	USSR Z3	USSR Z4	Z5	SST	CCT	JST	GST	USSR Z10	ID LE
-12	-11	-10	-9	-8	-7	-6	-5	-4	-3	-2	-1 0 +1	+2	+3	+4	+5	+6	+7	+8	+9	+10	+11	+12	

Standard Time Zones   Hours to **SUBTRACT (−)ADD (+)** Standard Time Zones

PST: Pacific Standard Time	0	0	**PST**: Pacific Standard Time
YST: Yukon Standard Time	−1	+1	**MST**: Mountain Standard Time
CA/HT: Central Alaska & Hawaiian Time	−2	+2	**CST**: Central Standard Time
NT/BT: Nome Time/Bering Time	−3	+3	**EST**: Eastern Standard Time
IDLW: International Date Line West	−4	+4	**AST**: Atlantic Standard Time
IDLE: International Date Line East	−5	+4½	**NFT**: Newfoundland Time
USSR Zone 10	−6	+5	**BST**: Brazil Standard Time
GST: Guam Standard Time	−7	+6	**AT**: Azores Time
SAST: South Australian Standard Time	−7½	+7	**WAT**: West African Time
JST: Japanese Standard Time	−8	+8	**GMT**: Greenwich Mean Time
MT: Moluccas Time	−8½		**WET**: Western European Time (England)
CCT: China Coast Time	−9	+9	**CET**: Central Europe Time
JT: Java Time	−9½	+10	**EET**: Eastern Europe Time
SST: South Sumatra Time & USSR Zone 6	−10	+11	**BT**: Bagdhad Time
NST: North Sumatra Time	−10½	+11½	**IT**: Iran Time
USSR Zone 5	−11	+12	**USSR** Zone 3
IST: Indian Standard Time	−11½		
USSR Zone 4	−12		

All times in this calendar are calculated from the West Coast of North America.*

Time changes (center two columns) are calculated from Pacific Standard Time (Zone 8) as Zero Point for this calendar.

Pacific Daylight Time (PDT or Standard Zone 7) is between April 4 and October 31, 1993.

If your time zone uses Daylight Savings Time, use the numbers given in this chart to calculate the number of hours to add (Eastward) or subtract (Westward) for the correct time in your area at all times.

If your time zones uses Standard Time year-round, use the numbers given for the time zone directly East of you during the time change (April 4 to October 31, 1993) when Daylight Savings Time is in effect.

Example: if you are in Western Europe, use Central European Time to calculate the correct time for your area from April 4 to October 31. Write this number on the inside cover for easy reference.

*Hours to add for the East Coast (EST/EDT) and for Greenwich Mean Time (GMT) are given at the bottom of each calendar page. Otherwise use the above chart for your time zone.

With this We'Moon, We Cast a Circle

With this **We'Moon**, we cast a circle,
With the moon we cast a circle around earth.
We hold this space sacred: the whole earth.
We enter the wheel of this year together,
on a journey through the next 13 Moons,
each in her own way,
with this **We'Moon,**
we cast a circle.

Wemoon come from all directions, wemoon come.
We come from earth, water, air and fire—all transforming.
We are root, stem, leaf, fruit and flower—all different
parts of one whole, each one flowing into the other.
Many waves, one ocean; many oceans one wave
of wemoon rising in all our colors, like earth
we are black, brown, red, yellow, white and gray.
All shapes, all sizes, all ages, in all stages
we feel our earth bodies connect with the Mother
we reach down inside to our common center
we circle around, like the Moon,
we cast a circle around the earth.

Wemoon invoke spirit in every way.
We call out, we go in, we dance, we spin,
we do what we do for the Goddess to come through:
Calling by whatever name we choose: Come, be with us now!
Oh, spirits of the directions, all elements,
guardians of the gateways, guide us now
as we journey the cycle of Moons to come.
We offer our heart songs in pictures and in poems,
in the magic we share, leafing through the pages
of this year, in the stories our lives tell.
We raise power in rhythm with the sun and the moon,
marking time with earth cycles, and all our relations.
The art of wemoon invites our presence,
inspires us to be creative, invokes the power within.
We raise our spirits in wemoon community.

To open the pathways of the coming Moon cycles,
13 wemoon spiral into the center, each one carrying a Moon
that bears a gift of the Mother.

They lay them down around the fire,
a string of pearls, asking all to look
into the heart of each Moon.
Each one is a pathway to spirit
that wemoon create. Taste her nectar, they say,
as they pass it around. Naming each one,
they invoke her spirit:

EARTH MOTHER MOON: *let us be at home with you.*
MOON OF VISIONS: *may we see through your clear eye
     how to live our visions.*
DREAMING MOON: *let the veil of illusion slip away.*
EARTH LOVING MOON: *may we embody the spirit of love.*
PRAYER MOON: *in beauty we seek you,
     help us to know what we are asking.*
MOON OF MUSES: *inspire us with your divine creativity.*
MOON OF FLOW: *let us feel our oneness with you.*
CELEBRATION MOON: *sing out with a joyful heart.*
EVERYDAY MAGIC MOON: *we see you in all we do.*
MEDITATION MOON: *let us hear you in the silence.*
SHAPE-SHIFTING MOON: *journey with us to the depths
     that we may find wholeness.*
ORACLE MOON: *open the way to our truth.*
ELEMENTALS MOON: *introduce us to your many spirit
     realms.*

13 Moons now lay in the center.
Here are the Moon paths we are about to enter.
The 13 wemoon turn to spiral out,
and the spiral dance of this year begins.
In gratitude, we follow the spirit pathways
opened through the offerings of wemoon.
Now we open the calendar pages and make
our way through the coming Moon cycles.
We are not alone; 13,000 wemoon join in this circle.
Together, we have great power to invoke spirit
in the worlds we share—may we use it with care.
The circle is open yet unbroken.
May the peace of the Goddess go in our hearts,
and the gift of Her presence be given.
Merry meet, merry part, and merry meet again.
Touch the earth. We are one. Blessed be.

Musawa

Homeself, Sacredself

I would counsel you to be still
To move away from everything for a time
To wait quietly until you come home to yourself

There will be signs

Songs will sing from your lips
Your body will dance with you
Your eyes will see magic
Where you keep the fresh flower
Where you burn the candle
Also where you cry and where you bleed

There will be signs

The magic of your homeself, your sacredself
Will take you to the sky
Luna will welcome your flight
With silver embraces
Comets will be your lovers

Trails of stars will carry you inward
Until, at your core, a cataclysm will burst
In celebration of homecoming
To the magic of your soul

© *Ila Suzanne 1986*

I. EARTH MOTHER MOON
let us be at home with you

December

♐♐♐

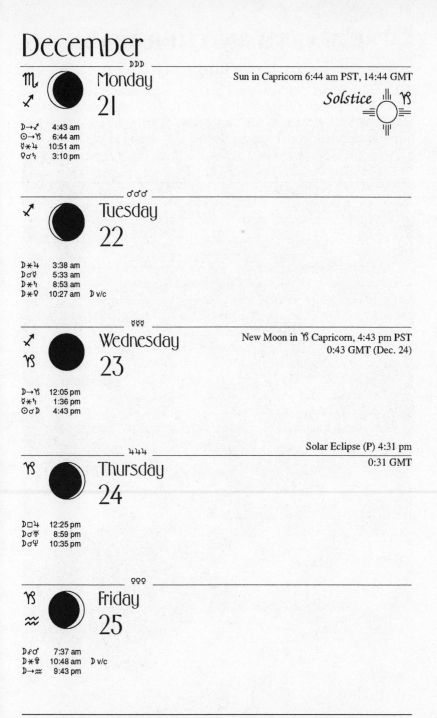

♏
♐
Monday
21

Sun in Capricorn 6:44 am PST, 14:44 GMT

Solstice ☷ ♑

☽→♐ 4:43 am
☉→♑ 6:44 am
☿✶♃ 10:51 am
♀☌♄ 3:10 pm

♂♂♂

♐
Tuesday
22

☽✶♃ 3:38 am
☽☌♅ 5:33 am
☽✶♄ 8:53 am
☽✶♀ 10:27 am ☽ v/c

☿☿☿

♐
♑
Wednesday
23

New Moon in ♑ Capricorn, 4:43 pm PST
0:43 GMT (Dec. 24)

☽→♑ 12:05 pm
☿✶♄ 1:36 pm
☉☌☽ 4:43 pm

♃♃♃

♑
Thursday
24

Solar Eclipse (P) 4:31 pm
0:31 GMT

☽□♃ 12:25 pm
☽☌♅ 8:59 pm
☽☌♆ 10:35 pm

♀♀♀

♑
♒
Friday
25

☽☍♂ 7:37 am
☽✶♀ 10:48 am ☽ v/c
☽→♒ 9:43 pm

All aspects in Pacific Standard Time; add 3 hours for EST; add 8 hours for GMT

CAPRICORN - *Mountain*   (DECEMBER 21—JANUARY 18)

Capricorn is really rocking and rolling with the times. With the unavoidable, overwhelming Uranus/Neptune series of conjunctions in your own sign, if you are just plodding along slowly towards the top of the mountain, you are missing the point! Major surprises, total changes in direction, new roles to play, crazy opportunities... you'll make it if you can live in the moment, stay open and adaptable. There is genius to be found in being, rather than in doing.

Uranus/Neptune rules all non-normal states of consciousness, both positive and negative. They manifest in disconcerting and disorienting moments of clarity, where you see the world as you've expected it, even built it, falling apart. Your temptation may be to retreat into the material world, acquiring things, hoarding position/power—trying to shore up your sense of dissolving self.

Depression is one stage of this process, where you reflect upon some crystallized structure of your life that is preventing further growth. You could discover a large part of your life to date suddenly becoming irrelevant. Actually a new dimension of your personality is coming forward; energy is being withdrawn from your existing life for a creative purpose.

With Jupiter at the peak of your chart and Uranus/Neptune in Capricorn, you're going to attract attention even if you don't know what you are doing.

At this time you are charismatic and exotic, with a hint of illusion/unreality which can be quite magnetic. You'll be in the public eye, bringing enthusiasm, high energy, vision and insight. It is time to rise to the social or professional occasion, this is an opportunity to contribute something of value to others in terms of your own personality and uniqueness. Expect the setting to be zany.

© *Gretchen Lawlor 1992*

≈ Saturday
26

D△4   11:31 pm

≈ Sunday
27

D♂ħ   5:10 am
D⚹♅   4:32 pm
D♂♀   5:58 pm
D□☿   10:23 pm   D v/c

© *Sudie Rakusin 1987*
from *"Dreams & Shadows"*

Dezember

ⅮⅮⅮ

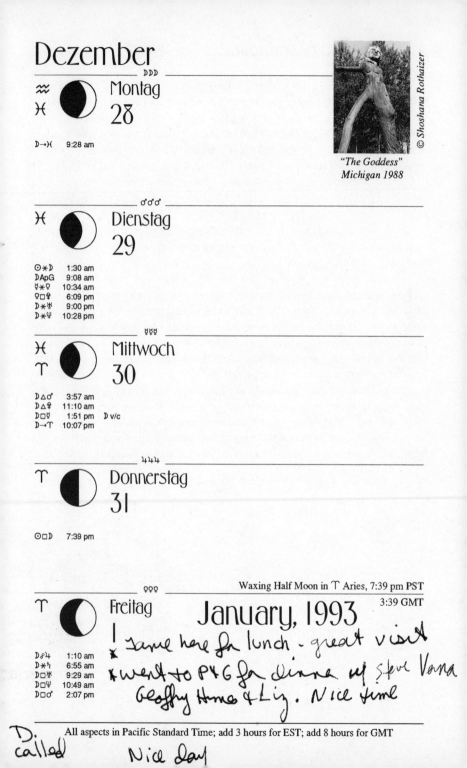

© Shoshana Rothaizer

"The Goddess"
Michigan 1988

♒
♓ **Montag**
28

☽→♓   9:28 am

♂♂♂

♓ **Dienstag**
29

☉✳☽   1:30 am
☽ApG   9:08 am
☿✳♀   10:34 am
♀□♀   6:09 pm
☽✳♅   9:00 pm
☽✳♆   10:28 pm

☿☿☿

♓
♈ **Mittwoch**
30

☽△♂   3:57 am
☽△♀   11:10 am
☽□♅   1:51 pm   ☽ v/c
☽→♈   10:07 pm

♃♃♃

♈ **Donnerstag**
31

☉□☽   7:39 pm

♀♀♀

Waxing Half Moon in ♈ Aries, 7:39 pm PST
3:39 GMT

♈ **Freitag**
January, 1993

☽☍♃   1:10 am
☽✳♄   6:55 am
☽□♅   9:29 am
☽□♆   10:49 am
☽□♂   2:07 pm

came here for lunch - great visit
went to P&G for dinner w/ Steve Vana
Geoffry Hamas & Liz. Nice time

All aspects in Pacific Standard Time; add 3 hours for EST; add 8 hours for GMT

D.
called

Nice Day

Lunar Cromlech of Wales   © Monica Sjoo 1991

Sacred Space: *The ancients held rituals in stone circles, sacred groves and other power places. Established religions hold ceremonies in churches and temples. When wemoon create ritual, we usually need to begin by creating our own sacred space. Building an altar with specially meaningful objects; casting a circle with salt water, incense, or light; calling in the directions and elements; invoking what we name as sacred—all are ways to help us to create a container for us to "go between the worlds" and connect with spirit.*   musawa

---

♈   Samstag
♉   2

☽⚹♀	6:32 am
♉→♑	6:48 am ☽ v/c
☽→♉	9:30 am
☽△♅	9:53 am

♉   Sonntag
     3

♂PrG	5:33 am
☉△☽	11:09 am
♀→♓	3:54 pm
☽□♄	5:13 pm
☉□♃	6:05 pm
☽△♅	7:25 pm
☽△♀	8:34 pm
☽⚹♂	9:48 pm

janvier

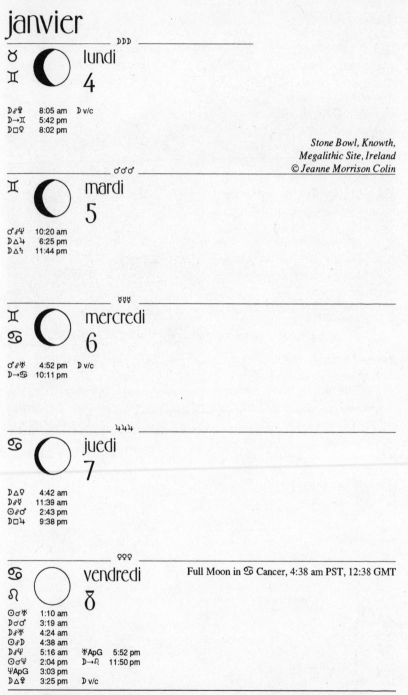

ℝℝℝ

♉
♊

lundi
4

D☍♀	8:05 am	D v/c
D→♊	5:42 pm	
D□♀	8:02 pm	

*Stone Bowl, Knowth,
Megalithic Site, Ireland
© Jeanne Morrison Colin*

♂♂♂

♊

mardi
5

♂☍♆	10:20 am
D△♃	6:25 pm
D△♄	11:44 pm

☿☿☿

♊
♋

mercredi
6

| ♂☍♅ | 4:52 pm | D v/c |
| D→♋ | 10:11 pm | |

♃♃♃

♋

juedi
7

D△♀	4:42 am
D☍♅	11:39 am
☉☍♂	2:43 pm
D□♃	9:38 pm

♀♀♀

♋
♌

vendredi
8

Full Moon in ♋ Cancer, 4:38 am PST, 12:38 GMT

☉♂♅	1:10 am		
D♂♂	3:19 am		
D☍♅	4:24 am		
☉☍D	4:38 am		
D☍♆	5:16 am	♅ApG	5:52 pm
☉♂♆	2:04 pm	D→♌	11:50 pm
♆ApG	3:03 pm		
D△♀	3:25 pm	D v/c	

All aspects in Pacific Standard Time; add 3 hours for EST; add 8 hours for GMT

OAK (Quercus)

The very image of this tree creates feelings of connection and grounding. The oak sends its roots deep into the earth and is extremely long lived. For centuries the oak has been used ritually to take on the illness of humans or to draw off disease. This was done within the sacred grove of oaks by placing an image of the person needing healing in the tree or by passing the actual part of the body needing healing through the fairy holes, (hollows where branches have rotted away). Fires made of oak wood were also used to warm the house of anyone ill to draw out the illness. A tea made of 1 part oak bark to 5 parts water, simmered 15 minutes then steeped for an hour to overnight is very astringent and can be used as a wash on wet itchy skin problems such as poison oak. Oak is associated with Rhea, Cybele and Hecate.

© *Colette Gardiner 1992*

Under a grandmother oak I create an altar. I plant the soles of my feet in cool black earth and pray.

Diana Rose Hartmann

© *Laura Anderson*

ॐ ◯ samedi
9

☽✳♃ 10:44 pm

ॐ ◐ dimanche
10

☽☌♄ 3:58 am
☽PrG 4:11 am
☽□♀ 4:05 pm   ☽ v/c

enero

☉ *Boudykke 1990*

ↅↅↅ

♌
♍ 　 ◗ 　 lunes
　　　　　 11

D→♍　0:21 am
♅□♃　10:37 am
D☍♀　2:18 pm

♂♂♂

♍ 　 ◗ 　 martes
　　　　 12

D△♀　1:03 am
D⚹♂　2:14 am
D△♅　6:15 am
D△♆　6:58 am
♅☍♂　10:00 am
☉△D　1:24 pm
D⚹♀　5:06 pm　　D v/c

☿☿☿

♍
♎ 　 ◑ 　 miercoles
　　　　 13

D→♎　1:31 am

♃♃♃

♎ 　 ◑ 　 jueves
　　　　 14

D☌♃　1:42 am
♅☌♆　2:21 am
D□♂　3:01 am
D△♄　7:40 am
♅☌♆　8:25 am
D□♅　8:45 am　　☉⚹♀　7:24 pm
D□♆　9:26 am　　☉□D　8:02 pm　　D v/c
D□♅　9:33 am

Waning Half Moon in ♎ Libra, 8:02 pm PST
4:02 GMT

♀♀♀

♎
♏ 　 ◑ 　 viernes
　　　　 15

D→♏　4:42 am
♂□♃　11:46 pm

All aspects in Pacific Standard Time; add 3 hours for EST; add 8 hours for GMT

Spirit Shelter—the Yurt

Stepping inside a circular we'moon space invokes a sense of spiritual expansiveness. The yurt, designed by the nomadic Mongol tribes in northern China, draws the eye upward to the sky, as in a tipi or kiva. The connection with the native spirits, four-leggeds and winds is close with the thin veil of the canvas and supporting lattice. A greenhouse for the soul to grow and bloom.

Willow Elliot 1991

♏	🌓	sabado
		16

☽△♀	4:28 am
☽△♂	6:06 am
⚷ApG	9:49 am
☽□♄	12:52 pm	♀△♂	8:42 pm
☽✶♅	1:47 pm	☽✶♄	9:45 pm
☽✶♆	2:24 pm

⊙⊙⊙

♏	🌓	domingo
♐		17

☽♂♄	1:27 am
⊙✶☽	5:53 am	☽ v/c
☽→♐	10:31 am

January

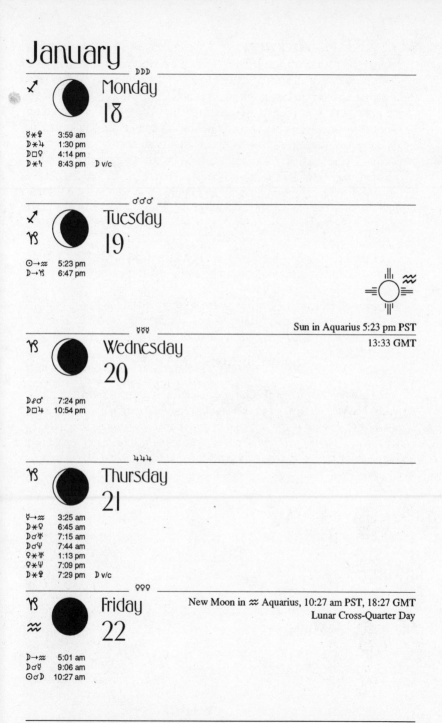

♐ **Monday** 18

☿⚹♀	3:59 am
☽⚹♃	1:30 pm
☽□♀	4:14 pm
☽⚹♄	8:43 pm	☽ v/c

♐ ♑ **Tuesday** 19

| ☉→♒ | 5:23 pm |
| ☽→♑ | 6:47 pm |

Sun in Aquarius 5:23 pm PST
13:33 GMT

♑ **Wednesday** 20

| ☽☍♂ | 7:24 pm |
| ☽□♃ | 10:54 pm |

♑ **Thursday** 21

☿→♒	3:25 am
☽⚹♀	6:45 am
☽♂♅	7:15 am
☽♂♆	7:44 am
♀⚹♅	1:13 pm
♀⚹♆	7:09 pm
☽⚹♀	7:29 pm	☽ v/c

♑ ♒ **Friday** 22

☽→♒	5:01 am
☽♂♅	9:06 am
☉♂☽	10:27 am

New Moon in ♒ Aquarius, 10:27 am PST, 18:27 GMT
Lunar Cross-Quarter Day

All aspects in Pacific Standard Time; add 3 hours for EST; add 8 hours for GMT

AQUARIUS - *Airwaves*   (JANUARY 19—FEBRUARY 17)

Aquarius can't just talk about it in '93, you have to be out there getting your hands dirty—doing it! Saturn continues to move through Aquarius this year (briefly progressing into Pisces during May and June), pushing you to take a stance upon your ever present Aquarian idealism. Your role in any group becomes more obvious as you seek to hold the group to those humanitarian, egalitarian visions appearing in your dreams and meditations.

You are trying your hardest to live your principles in the most tangible ways possible, yet there is a lot of resistance to doing this. For one, you are also in an introspective phase, needing plenty of solitude. You aren't easy to reach. Whittle away at old obligations, finish old business and look for the most cryptic ways to get your message out. Struggles in your personal life will affect your public image.

Your public image has been undergoing transformation for quite a while now, as you peel off layers of responsibility and power that are no longer useful to you; you crave a simple life.

Philosophy, metaphysics, religion, the study of other cultures is emphasized as Jupiter transits your solar 9th house. Travel is valuable in that it expands your world view immediately and intimately (especially likely August-September). Foreigners will feature, collaborative efforts may be achieved with a partner half way across the world. You may feel more at home anywhere than at home. Your role as teacher is important in 1993.

Opportunities to retreat, to meditate and contemplate, time with a therapist—all these are particularly helpful. You need some way to reflect on the flashes of insight that have been occurring with increasing frequency since 1991. This is a year for tremendous shifts of consciousness—make sure you are peaceful enough to appreciate them.

© Gretchen Lawlor 1992

♒   ●   **Saturday 23**

⊙♂♅   7:42 am
☽△♃   10:03 am
☽♂♄   6:37 pm

♒   ◐   **Sunday 24**
♓

☽□♀   7:09 am   ☽ v/c
☽→♓   4:48 pm

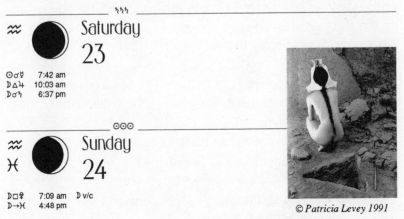

© Patricia Levey 1991

Rainbow Woman Comes...

...I was very peaceful, resting there, when out of nowhere a woman appeared beside me, older than me perhaps, yet radiantly ageless. Her hair was raven black and plaited in long braids.... She stood there quietly, looking into my soul with an almost palpable love...

...At the same time, upon the highest part of the mountain, I saw a trail of light begin to wind down toward me along the trail. Drumbeats began, very soft, so that I turned my ear to listen closely. As this light drew nearer, I saw that it was the ancient Grandmothers, dancing in their slow and gentle step down the mountain—each one so bright in spirit that her aura blended with the next, forming a continuous line. The White-hairs, the Wisdom Women, the lineage of light and love—dancing down, dancing down, dancing down...

...As the ancient ones came near where I was sitting, the leader veered off and began to dance around me in a circle. As the circle closed and they continued their movement, there suddenly appeared within this outer circle another circle. The second circle was composed of young women of my age and time, some of whom I joyfully recognized. They too were shining with brilliant light, and they too were dancing. As the motion continued, the circles of women began to weave in and out of each other, swaying in and through, blending and separating.

Within those circles there came yet another one formed of seven Grandmothers—white-haired women, women who were significant to me, powerful old women. They danced close around Rainbow Woman and me. Looking up at their beautifully lined faces, I felt the love that bonded us all...

...As I brought my attention back down, the circles around me faded and disappeared, and I found myself alone again with Rainbow Woman. Once again she stood quietly for a moment, filling my senses with the beauty of her form and spirit, and then an amazing communication began.

© *Brooke Medicine Eagle 1991, excerpted from* Buffalo Woman Comes Singing

II. MOON OF VISIONS
may we see through your clear eye
how to live our visions

Shaman Calling Her Allies   © *Vicki Ledray Grabicki 1990*

Another way of leaking the power of our inner consciousness is to get caught on the detour of the Great Visions Path. This is one where we are constantly seeking the "great vision", thinking that this will change our lives, transform all our weaknesses, and heal all our ills. What is forgotten on this detour is that the integration of the vision into our lives is up to us, and in that actual practice lies the transformation. It is often easier to open ourselves to receive such a vision than to put it into practice.

© *Brooke Medicine Eagle 1991, excerpted from* Buffalo Woman Comes Singing

Januar

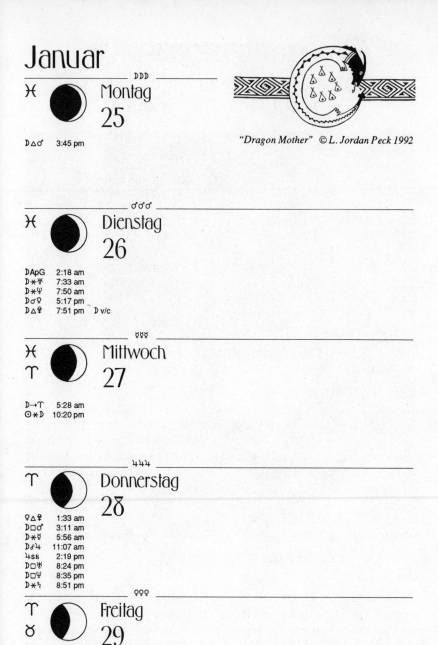

♓ 🌑 ☽☽☽ **Montag**
25

☽△♂ 3:45 pm

"Dragon Mother" © *L. Jordan Peck 1992*

♓ 🌒 ♂♂♂ **Dienstag**
26

☽ApG   2:18 am
☽✳♅   7:33 am
☽✳♆   7:50 am
☽♂♀   5:17 pm
☽△♀   7:51 pm   ☽ v/c

♓
♈ 🌓 ☿☿☿ **Mittwoch**
27

☽→♈   5:28 am
☉✳☽ 10:20 pm

♈ 🌓 ♃♃♃ **Donnerstag**
28

♀△♀   1:33 am
☽□♂   3:11 am
☽✳♅   5:56 am
☽♂♃ 11:07 am
♃sʀ   2:19 pm
☽□♅   8:24 pm
☽□♆   8:35 pm
☽✳♄   8:51 pm

♈
♉ 🌔 ♀♀♀ **Freitag**
29

♀△♃   5:25 pm   ☽ v/c
☽→♉   5:37 pm

All aspects in Pacific Standard Time; add 3 hours for EST; add 8 hours for GMT

(Mask) © Lillian Pitt

Reenacting Your Vision

One of the most powerful things that people who work actively with their dreams have learned to do is to gather a circle of friends to act out a particularly powerful dream or vision they have received. This kind of sacred theater is one of the oldest of human rituals—from animal dances painted on the walls of Ice Age caves, to the yearly round of dances of the Katchina Spirits of the Hopi.

© *Brooke Medicine Eagle 1991, excerpted from* Buffalo Woman Comes Singing

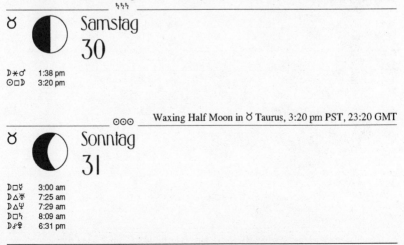

♉	Samstag 30	
☽✶♂	1:38 pm	
☉□☽	3:20 pm	

Waxing Half Moon in ♉ Taurus, 3:20 pm PST, 23:20 GMT

♉	Sonntag 31	
☽□☿	3:00 am	
☽△♅	7:25 am	
☽△♆	7:29 am	
☽□♄	8:09 am	
☽☍♀	6:31 pm	

fevrier

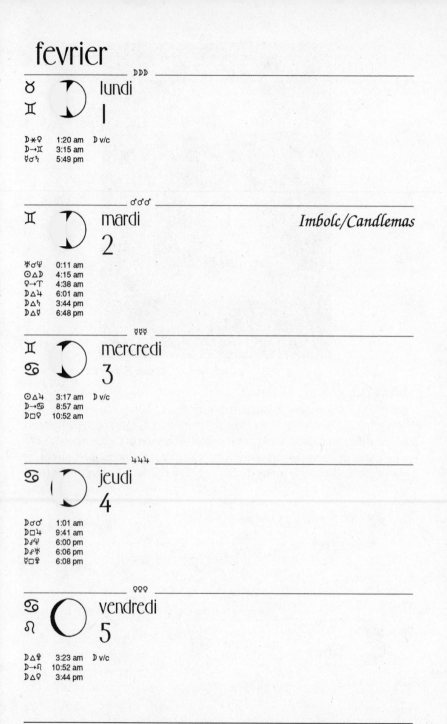

DDD

ŏ ☽ **lundi**
Ⅱ   **1**

D⚹♀ 1:20 am   D v/c
D→Ⅱ 3:15 am
ŏ♂♄ 5:49 pm

♂♂♂

Ⅱ ☽ **mardi**
      2   *Imbolc/Candlemas*

♅♂Ψ 0:11 am
☉△D 4:15 am
♀→♈ 4:38 am
D△♃ 6:01 am
D△♄ 3:44 pm
D△ŏ 6:48 pm

☿☿☿

Ⅱ ☽ **mercredi**
♋   **3**

☉△♃ 3:17 am   D v/c
D→♋ 8:57 am
D□♀ 10:52 am

♃♃♃

♋ ☽ **jeudi**
      4

D♂♂ 1:01 am
D□♃ 9:41 am
D☍Ψ 6:00 pm
D☍♅ 6:06 pm
ŏ□♀ 6:08 pm

♀♀♀

♋ ○ **vendredi**
♌   **5**

D△♀ 3:23 am   D v/c
D→♌ 10:52 am
D△♀ 3:44 pm

All aspects in Pacific Standard Time; add 3 hours for EST; add 8 hours for GMT

Magdalene: Erz Hayyim Hi (She is the Tree of Life)
© *Carolyn Hillyer 1990*

Imbolc (Candlemas): Feast of the Flame

First of the four Cross-Quarter Holydays
Midpoint between Winter Solstice and Vernal Equinox
Theme: initiation, purification
Goddesses: Brigit—Goddess of fire, inspiration, healing, childbirth, poets, smithys, crafts wimmin; Cerridwen—Goddess of the Cauldron and fortress of wisdom; Dana—Goddess who has total command of fire and water; Inari—Goddess of fire and smithcraft; Imanja (Brazil); Februa (meaning purification).

© *Ffiona Morgan 1991, excerpt from* Wild Witches Don't Get the Blues

White Lady/Brigid with her Tree, Well, Stone & Tor
© Monica Sjoo 1989

Bride's Day / Imbolc on Isle of Lewis 1989

...She is also Brigid/Bride,
radiant White Maiden of early spring.
Sacred Fire, Moon & Sun being, serpent of Waters
giver of fertility to animals and plants,
the One who greens this now suffering Earth
& stirs the internal Kundalini
sexual menstrual fire in women.
we greeted you here in your season,
a grey and rainy dawn
at Bride's Well
by the stormy sea,
the beginning of a day of total magic
when all of Nature put on its finery
to celebrate and welcome back the Bride.

excerpt © Monica Sjoo 1989

EYEBRIGHT (Euphrasia officinalis)
Eyebright is an herb that works on both the physical and spiritual levels. A strong tea used as a wash helps clear eye infections. If you drink it, it gives you a clearer perspective on the world. Carry to increase psychic powers and when you need to see the truth of the matter.   © Colette Gardiner 1992

♌ ○ **samedi**
6

☽✶♃ 10:09 am
☉☍☽ 3:56 pm
☽☍♄ 7:44 pm

Full Moon in ♌ Leo, 3:56 pm PST, 23:56 GMT

♌
♍ ◐ **dimanche**
7

☽□♀ 3:16 am
♅→♓ 8:20 am ☽ v/c
☽→♍ 10:29 am
☽☍♅ 10:47 am
☽PrG 12:33 pm

febrero

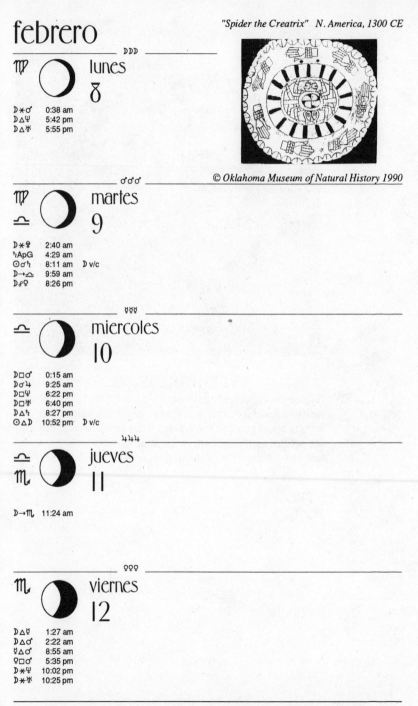

"Spider the Creatrix" N. America, 1300 CE

© *Oklahoma Museum of Natural History 1990*

ᛞᛞᛞ

♍ ○ **lunes**
8

☽✶♂	0:38 am
☽△♆	5:42 pm
☽△♅	5:55 pm

♂♂♂

♍ ☽ **martes**
♎ **9**

☽✶♀	2:40 am	
♄ApG	4:29 am	
☉♂♄	8:11 am	☽ v/c
☽→♎	9:59 am	
☽☍♀	8:26 pm	

☿☿☿

♎ ☽ **miercoles**
10

☽□♂	0:15 am	
☽♂♃	9:25 am	
☽□♆	6:22 pm	
☽□♅	6:40 pm	
☽△♄	8:27 pm	
☉△☽	10:52 pm	☽ v/c

♃♃♃

♎ ☽ **jueves**
♏ **11**

☽→♏	11:24 am

♀♀♀

♏ ☽ **viernes**
12

☽△♅	1:27 am
☽△♂	2:22 am
☿△♂	8:55 am
♀□♂	5:35 pm
☽✶♆	10:02 pm
☽✶♅	10:25 pm

All aspects in Pacific Standard Time; add 3 hours for EST; add 8 hours for GMT

Spider Womon and Her Web: A Lesbian Vision

...I was freshly come from my celtic land of ancient sacred rocks and sea, land deeply imbedded in my bones; a huge part of me formed, informed by that spirit-filled landscape.

I lay between the worlds of dark and morning light, in the high dry mountain land of Colorado; still jet-lagged, not yet awake, not asleep.

All at once I was aware of the Earth in all her roundness in front of me. Above and to her left, very close to her, was a hugely powerful shining presence. As I looked, amazed, I heard/felt very strongly the words, "I am Spider Womon." I was awed by the power of her presence. I looked at the Earth again. All over her, touching her, was Spider Womon's web, the strands hanging broken and limp. Then I heard Spider Womon say, "Whenever wemoon meet, open their hearts to each other, touch deeply, a strand is mended."

As I heard this I felt, deep in my belly, something jolt, join, reconnect, come together. When this happened I saw the Web become whole, complete.

Instantly, shimmering, sparkling, iridescent energy was rushing, pouring through every strand.

My hands reached out gently, feeling the energy surrounding the Earth. I knew, because the Web had been mended, become complete again, that everything was different. New possibilities existed. What had happened before was no longer possible. My other mind said, "Rape in its many forms is no longer possible."

At that moment the vision faded. I lay looking at the delicate pre-dawn morning light through the window, filled with a sense of a different knowledge, of having been gifted, shown something extraordinary....

excerpt, © Boa Snake ♀, 1992

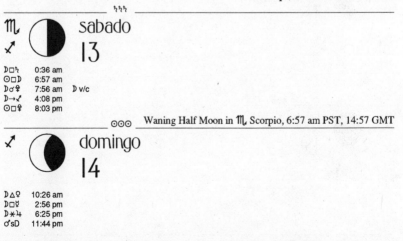

♏ ♐ ☽ sabado
13

☽□♄ 0:36 am
☉□☽ 6:57 am
☽♂♀ 7:56 am   ☽ v/c
☽→♐ 4:08 pm
☉♏♀ 8:03 pm

⊙⊙⊙ Waning Half Moon in ♏ Scorpio, 6:57 am PST, 14:57 GMT

♐ ☽ domingo
14

☽△♀ 10:26 am
☽□♅ 2:56 pm
☽✱♃ 6:25 pm
♂sD 11:44 pm

February

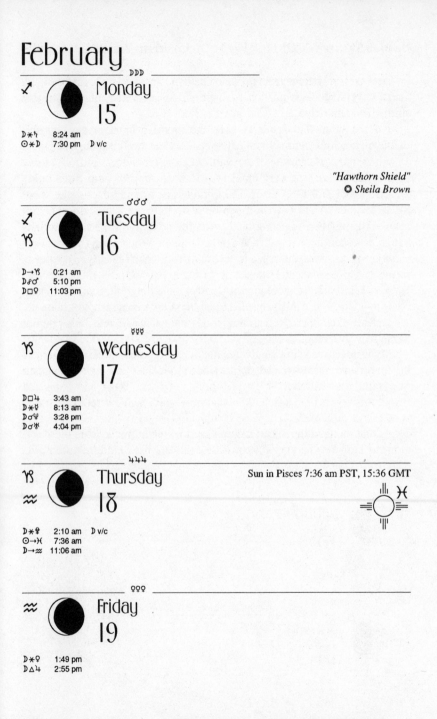

☽☽☽
♐ **Monday**
15

☽⚹♄ 8:24 am
☉⚹☽ 7:30 pm ☽ v/c

"Hawthorn Shield"
✹ *Sheila Brown*

♂♂♂
♐
♑ **Tuesday**
16

☽→♑ 0:21 am
☽☍♂ 5:10 pm
☽□♀ 11:03 pm

☿☿☿
♑ **Wednesday**
17

☽□♃ 3:43 am
☽⚹♅ 8:13 am
☽☌♆ 3:28 pm
☽☌♇ 4:04 pm

♃♃♃
♑
♒ **Thursday**
18

Sun in Pisces 7:36 am PST, 15:36 GMT

☽⚹♀ 2:10 am ☽ v/c
☉→♓ 7:36 am
☽→♒ 11:06 am

♀♀♀
♒ **Friday**
19

☽⚹♀ 1:49 pm
☽△♃ 2:55 pm

All aspects in Pacific Standard Time; add 3 hours for EST; add 8 hours for GMT

PISCES - *Ocean*

Pisces sets a different course in the 90's. Do not try to push ahead in the outer world, it is a time of completion, of endings. You are being called to explore the subtlety and richness of your private, inner life.

You are tempted to despair over failures, wallow in victim/martyr roles. Come to terms with parts of your life that have served their purpose, give thanks for all you have gained from them, and let them go.

Pluto takes you down fast, crashing to the bottom of the heap socially and professionally, only to bring you back up again in a few years—even more potent than before, but with a much more personal flavor. Resist any shortcuts here, be scrupulously honest, take a hard and critical look at any good business offers presented to you now.

You will surprise yourself (as well as others) with the grace you display as you accept the monumental changes occurring in your life now. If you need any assistance, just ask; you will get it.

The dominating 1993 aspect, Uranus conjunct Neptune in Capricorn, brings insights into goals and roles beyond your wildest dreams. Your visions are utopian, heralding union with others for humanitarian or social purposes. You struggle to find your own footing involved with such a group—either you will push for new freedom/new possibilities within it, or you will rebel against their standards and seek other company.

By the end of 1993 you will be a student again. Opportunities appear to travel, write, and even lecture. Be humble about your limits. You are being reminded that something greater than you exists which is running the show. Strive for the immediate goals. Focus on locally based projects. Start small, but get started.

© Gretchen Lawlor 1992

♒		Saturday
♓		20

☽☌♄	7:36 am
♀☍♃	9:21 am
☿✳︎♇	9:40 am
☽☐♀	2:10 pm
☿✳︎♅	6:08 pm ☽ v/c
☽→♓	11:12 pm

♓		Sunday
		21

| ☉☌☽ | 5:06 am |
| ☽△♂ | 5:16 pm |

© Boa Snake ♀

Dreamer

I am sister of the Moon
Daughter of the Sea
Tossed by aqua and
Drenched with white light,
I am child of the green and ancient trees
Telling stories of
Sacred stones
Singing songs of
Wind-swept summers.
Once upon a high hill
I beheld the unraveling of
Comets
And followed their long tails down into
A valley porcelain with the Moon's shadows.
There the sleepless flowers
Gathered up the comet's
Night brilliance and strung it all together
Like liquid pearls on a strand,
Like Ariadne's jeweled crown.

I am daughter of the Sea
Sister of the Moon
Called forth to inhabit the halls of
My ancestors
Who dreaming deep
Dreamed me.

Jan Larsson

III. DREAMING MOON
let the veil of illusion slip away

Dreams are filled with omens. Listen, learn, fear not.

Februar

♓ **Montag**

22

ⅅApG	9:54 am
ⅅ✳Ψ	4:05 pm
ⅅ✳♅	4:53 pm
ⅅ☌♅	8:28 pm

♓
♈ **Dienstag**

23

ⅅ△♀	2:47 am	ⅅ v/c
ⅅ→♈	11:51 am	

♈ **Mittwoch**

24

ⅅ☐♂	6:25 am
ⅅ☍♃	3:15 pm
ⅅ☌♀	8:48 pm

♈ **Donnerstag**

25

ⅅ☐Ψ	4:48 am	
ⅅ☐♅	5:41 am	
ⅅ✳♄	9:55 am	ⅅ v/c

♈
♉ **Freitag**

26

ⅅ→♉	0:12 am
♀SB	1:38 am
☉✳ⅅ	4:58 pm
ⅅ✳♂	7:02 pm

All aspects in Pacific Standard Time; add 3 hours for EST; add 8 hours for GMT

Healing Waters

my heart suspended in
the dipping bucket
well above the
water line

infinite ocean
of tears underground
current of ancient grief

slowly releasing the rope
touching the depth of empty
darkness

and so
i am washing
in the first waters of life

© Nancy Blair 1990

Night Flight
© A. Kimberlin Blackburn 1991

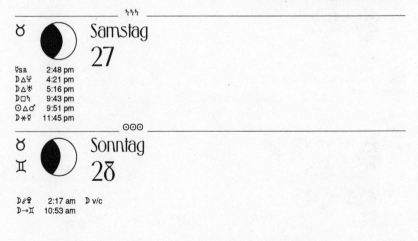

♉ Samstag
27

☿ SR	2:48 pm
☽ △ ♆	4:21 pm
☽ △ ♅	5:16 pm
☽ □ ♄	9:43 pm
☉ △ ♂	9:51 pm
☽ ✳ ☿	11:45 pm

♉
♊ Sonntag
28

| ☽ ☍ ♀ | 2:17 am | ☽ v/c |
| ☽ → ♊ | 10:53 am | |

mars

♌♌♌ ──────────

♊ ☽ lundi
1

☉□☽ 7:47 am
☽△♃ 11:38 am
☽✶♀ 9:20 pm

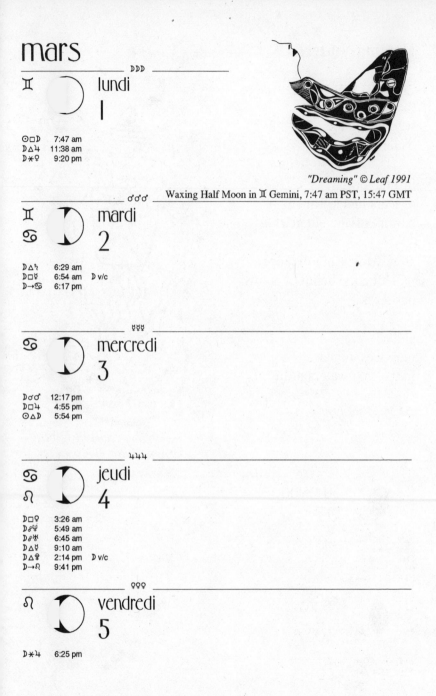

"Dreaming" © Leaf 1991

Waxing Half Moon in ♊ Gemini, 7:47 am PST, 15:47 GMT

─── ♂♂♂ ───

♊
♋ ☽ mardi
2

☽△♄ 6:29 am
☽□☿ 6:54 am   ☽ v/c
☽→♋ 6:17 pm

─── ☿☿☿ ───

♋ ☽ mercredi
3

☽☌♂ 12:17 pm
☽□♃ 4:55 pm
☉△☽ 5:54 pm

─── ♃♃♃ ───

♋
♌ ☽ jeudi
4

☽□♀ 3:26 am
☽☍♆ 5:49 am
☽☍♅ 6:45 am
☽△♅ 9:10 am
☽△♀ 2:14 pm   ☽ v/c
☽→♌ 9:41 pm

─── ♀♀♀ ───

♌ ☽ vendredi
5

☽✶♃ 6:25 pm

─────────────

All aspects in Pacific Standard Time; add 3 hours for EST; add 8 hours for GMT

© Mari Jackson 1991

MUGWORT (Artemesia Vulgare): Mugwort has long been a symbol of healing and psychic powers. A mild tea will help open the third eye and produce vivid dreams. The same effect can be achieved by placing a fresh or dry sprig near the bed or putting some dry herb in a pillow. Sacred to Artemis/ Diana.   © *Colette Gardiner 1992*

♌
♍

samedi
6

☿ ⚹ ♅	3:19 am
☽ △ ♀	5:22 am
☽ ☍ ♄	12:17 pm
☽ □ ♀	2:47 pm
☿ ⚹ ♆	6:44 pm ☽ v/c
☽ → ♍	9:53 pm

♍

dimanche
7

☽ ⚹ ♂   3:14 pm

marzo

In the night I sink below in you, waters catch and flow
© *A. Kimberlin Blackburn 1991*

‒‒‒‒‒‒‒ ☽☽☽ ‒‒‒‒‒‒‒

lunes 8

♍
♎

☽PrG	0:29 am
☉☍☽	1:46 am
☽☍♉	3:59 am
☽△♆	6:05 am
☽△♅	7:02 am
☽✳♀	1:43 pm
☉☌♉	8:01 pm ☽ v/c
☽→♎	8:47 pm

Full Moon in ♍ Virgo, 1:46 am PST, 9:46 GMT

‒‒‒‒‒‒‒ ♂♂♂ ‒‒‒‒‒‒‒

martes 9

♎

☽□☌♂	2:56 pm
☽☌♃	4:11 pm

‒‒‒‒‒‒‒ ☿☿☿ ‒‒‒‒‒‒‒

miercoles 10

♎
♏

☽☍♀	4:28 am
☽□♆	5:29 am
☽□♅	6:32 am
☽△♄	11:30 am ☽ v/c
☽→♏	8:40 pm
☉✳♆	9:34 pm

‒‒‒‒‒‒‒ ♃♃♃ ‒‒‒‒‒‒‒

jueves 11

♏

♀sʙ	1:25 am
☉✳♅	1:52 pm
☽△♂	4:38 pm
♂□♃	8:09 pm
☿PrG	9:31 pm
☽△♉	10:34 pm

‒‒‒‒‒‒‒ ♀♀♀ ‒‒‒‒‒‒‒

viernes 12

♏
♐

☽✳♆	7:22 am
☽✳♅	8:31 am
☉△☽	9:55 am
☽□♄	2:07 pm
☽☌♀	3:37 pm ☽ v/c
☽→♐	11:34 pm

All aspects in Pacific Standard Time; add 3 hours for EST; add 8 hours for GMT

one thing becomes another ❂ *Kiwani*

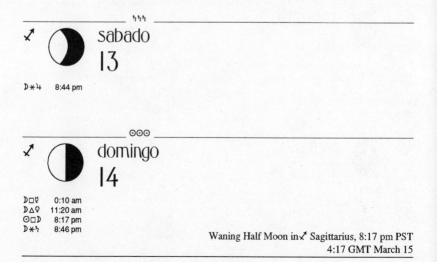

♐ sabado
13

☽✶♃   8:44 pm

♐ domingo
14

☽□♅   0:10 am
☽△♀   11:20 am
☉□☽   8:17 pm
☽✶♄   8:46 pm

Waning Half Moon in ♐ Sagittarius, 8:17 pm PST
4:17 GMT March 15

March

♐ ☽ **Monday**
♑   **15**

☿△♂ 1:18 am ☽ v/c
☽→♑ 6:28 am
☉△♀ 4:33 pm

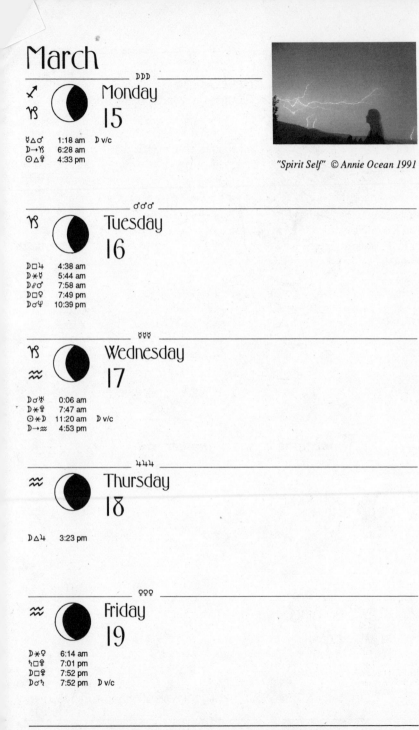

"Spirit Self" © *Annie Ocean 1991*

♂♂♂

♑ ☽ **Tuesday**
          16

☽□♃ 4:38 am
☽✳♉ 5:44 am
☽☍♂ 7:58 am
☽□♀ 7:49 pm
☽♂♆ 10:39 pm

☿☿☿

♑ ☽ **Wednesday**
♒   **17**

☽♂♅ 0:06 am
☽✳♀ 7:47 am
☉✳☽ 11:20 am ☽ v/c
☽→♒ 4:53 pm

♃♃♃

♒ ☽ **Thursday**
          18

☽△♃ 3:23 pm

♀♀♀

♒ ☽ **Friday**
          19

☽✳♀ 6:14 am
♄□♀ 7:01 pm
☽□♀ 7:52 pm
☽♂♄ 7:52 pm ☽ v/c

All aspects in Pacific Standard Time; add 3 hours for EST; add 8 hours for GMT

ARIES - *Spark*

Exciting times for all of us—1993 continues trends we've been feeling since 1991, and as the conjunction between Uranus and Neptune becomes exact this year, things heat up even more. Uranus and Neptune are planets better described in symbols than in words. Imagine Uranus as a lightning bolt illuminating the darkness for a moment. And what is revealed in that instant is Neptune the dissolver, in Capricorn, disintegrating walls, eroding boundaries— fleeting glimpses of a future very different from what we know now.

How does all this manifest for Aries? For years you've been obsessed with your social contribution—what is it you are supposed to be doing for the world? Sudden opportunities have appeared and as quickly disappeared or changed form. You may find yourself circling in closer and closer to an ideal. Now with Uranus exactly conjunct Neptune, you will experience moments where you really feel you've gotten there. You are a natural revolutionary; use it now to inspire others. There is a cause, a quest to be undertaken by a group you are involved with—remind them.

Unfortunately it is easy to be deluded and misled under such a configuration. Here are clues to help you with sorting it out in 1993. 1) If you've got something you really want to do, do it now. 2) If you are having difficulty finding that role or life direction, you are probably focusing too much on your individual importance. Saturn in Aquarius (1991-93), indicates you will struggle to balance your personal needs and your group allegiances. 3) You are the Initiator, but it is not the time to go it alone, or to pursue power for its own sake. Jupiter in Libra provides help through partnership /companionship; at times you'll need to temper your fiery ways.

© Gretchen Lawlor 1992

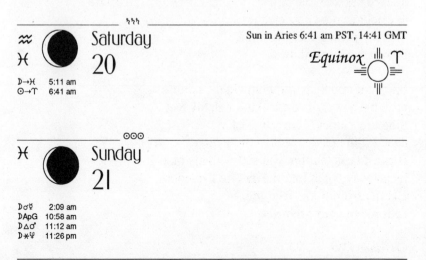

♒
♓

Saturday
20

☽→♓ 5:11 am
☉→♈ 6:41 am

Sun in Aries 6:41 am PST, 14:41 GMT

Equinox ♈

♓

Sunday
21

☽☌♉ 2:09 am
☽ApG 10:58 am
☽△♂ 11:12 am
☽✶♆ 11:26 pm

Invocation

Spirits of dawn, uncurling from the east,
breathe your cleansing air into my being.
Lift my spirit on the wings of phoenix,
fly me along my motherline
and raise me up to my own zenith.
Sweet burning cedar,
encircle me in your healing presence.
Air: bend me, shape me, fill me with peace.

Spirits of noon, radiating from the south,
spread your passionate fire into my heart.
This flame I hold connects me to you,
is my own inner light seeking expression.
Deepest fire at earth's core,
I feel your magma rising, erupting in me.
Fire: touch me, teach me, leap within me now!

Spirits of sunset, flowing from the west,
flood your nourishing water into the well of my soul.
I aim my tears into this chalice
and spill it on reclaimed land to nurture my source.
Sacred water coursing in me,
I dance naked in the rain
to celebrate our connectedness.
**Water: quench me, wash me,
drown me in rainbows!**

Spirits of midnight, throbbing in the north,
push the power of earth up through my feet.
Sing to me, rock, I am your sister;
dance with me, tree, I am your lover.
Blessed Gaia, nurture yourself with my blood,
recycle my bones into flowers for the moon.
**Earth: ground me, feed me,
root me in your embrace.**

IV. PRAYER MOON
in beauty we seek,
help us to know what we are asking for

© *Mari Jackson 1991*

Great Spirit, this tobacco between us
is smoke, is prayer—in this bowl between us
we hold everything there is, flame and hope.

In this bowl of tobacco are offerings and prayer,
we hold the presence of our ancestors here, we feel
the end of winter, the North letting go its grip:
the deaths, the aloneness, the fear, the losses,
what we've sacrificed, that now joy takes us...

excerpted from "Tobacco Prayer" from A Basket of Light
© *Melane Lohmann 1991*

Marz

...Day is a boat that will carry you some place new.

☺ *Sami Gray*

♓
♈

Montag
22

☽✶♅	1:03 am	
☿sD	5:38 am	
☽△♀	8:29 am	☽ v/c
☽→♈	5:52 pm	
☉☌☽	11:15 pm	

New Moon in ♈ Aries, 11:15 pm PST, 7:15 GMT

♈

Dienstag
23

☽☍♃	3:17 pm

♈

Mittwoch
24

☽□♂	1:24 am
☽☌♀	3:12 am
☽□♆	11:54 am
☽□♅	1:33 pm
☽✶♄	9:53 pm

♈
♉

Donnerstag
25

♀□♂	3:41 am	☽ v/c
☽→♉	6:00 am	

♉

Freitag
26

☽✶☿	3:46 am
☽✶♂	2:40 pm
☽△♆	11:17 pm

All aspects in Pacific Standard Time; add 3 hours for EST; add 8 hours for GMT

© *Patricia Levey 1991*

♉
♊ Samstag
27

☽△♅ 0:56 am
☽☍♀ 7:41 am
☽□♄ 9:25 am ☽ v/c
☽→♊ 4:48 pm

♊ Sonntag
28

☉⚹☽ 8:07 am
☽△♃ 11:58 am
☽□♉ 3:59 pm
☽⚹♀ 7:24 pm

mars

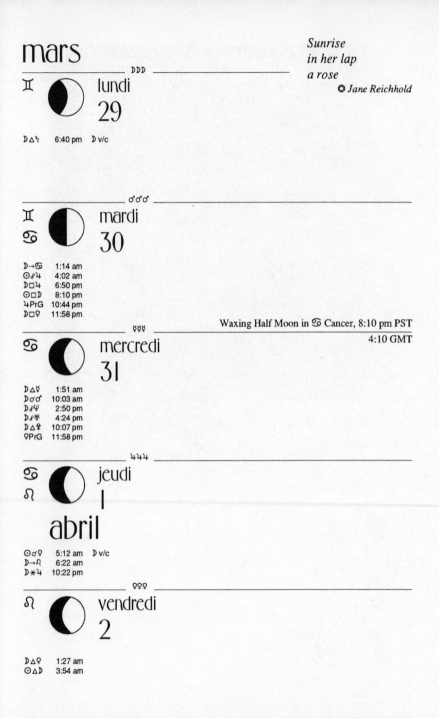

—————— ☽☽☽ ——————

♊   **lundi**
        29

☽△♄   6:40 pm   ☽ v/c

—————— ♂♂♂ ——————

♊
♋   **mardi**
        30

☽→♋   1:14 am
☉♂♄   4:02 am
☽□♄   6:50 pm
☉□☽   8:10 pm
♄PrG   10:44 pm
☽□♀   11:58 pm

Waxing Half Moon in ♋ Cancer, 8:10 pm PST
4:10 GMT

—————— ☿☿☿ ——————

♋   **mercredi**
        31

☽△♅   1:51 am
☽♂♂   10:03 am
☽♂♇   2:50 pm
☽♂♅   4:24 pm
☽△♀   10:07 pm
♀PrG   11:58 pm

—————— ♄♄♄ ——————

♋
♌   **jeudi**
        1

abril

☉♂♀   5:12 am   ☽ v/c
☽→♌   6:22 am
☽✳♄   10:22 pm

—————— ♀♀♀ ——————

♌   **vendredi**
        2

☽△♀   1:27 am
☉△☽   3:54 am

—————————————————————————

All aspects in Pacific Standard Time; add 3 hours for EST; add 8 hours for GMT

Seeding Prayer   © *Durga T. Bernhard 1985*

In ceremony, she greets each new day,
Kindling a small flame, touching the earth to pray...
Opening Lines from "In Ceremony"   ✺ *Linda Besant 1989*

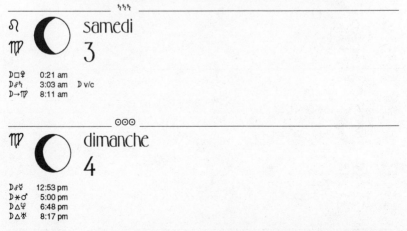

ሳሳሳ

♌   samedi
♍   3

☽□♀   0:21 am
☽☍♄   3:03 am   ☽ v/c
☽→♍   8:11 am

☉☉☉

♍   dimanche
      4

☽☍♅   12:53 pm
☽⚹♂   5:00 pm
☽△♆   6:48 pm
☽△♅   8:17 pm

Daylight Savings Time begins 2:00 am PST

abril

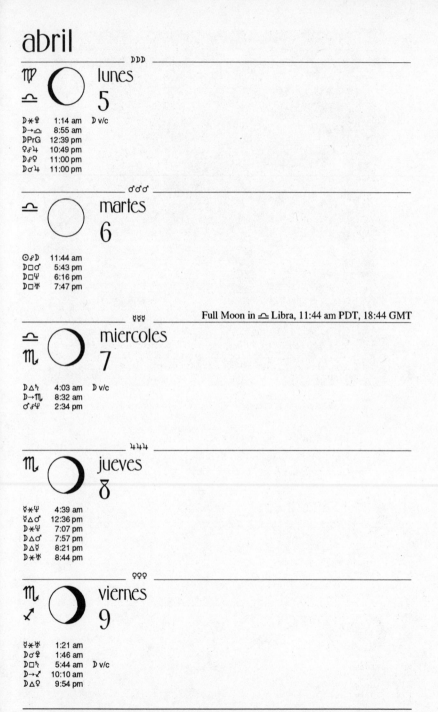

♍︎
♎︎

☽☽☽

lunes
5

☽⚹♀	1:14 am	☽ v/c
☽→♎︎	8:55 am	
☽PrG	12:39 pm	
☿☍♃	10:49 pm	
☽☍♀	11:00 pm	
☽☌♃	11:00 pm	

♎︎

♂♂♂

martes
6

☉☍☽	11:44 am
☽☐♂	5:43 pm
☽☐♆	6:16 pm
☽☐♅	7:47 pm

☿☿☿

Full Moon in ♎︎ Libra, 11:44 am PDT, 18:44 GMT

♎︎
♏︎

miercoles
7

☽△♄	4:03 am	☽ v/c
☽→♏︎	8:32 am	
♂☍♆	2:34 pm	

♃♃♃

♏︎

jueves
8

☿⚹♆	4:39 am
☿△♂	12:36 pm
☽⚹♆	7:07 pm
☽△♂	7:57 pm
☽△☿	8:21 pm
☽⚹♅	8:44 pm

♀♀♀

♏︎
♐︎

viernes
9

☿⚹♅	1:21 am	
☽☌♀	1:46 am	
☽☐♄	5:44 am	☽ v/c
☽→♐︎	10:10 am	
☽△♀	9:54 pm	

All aspects in Pacific Daylight Time; add 3 hours for EST; add 8 hours for GMT

She Speaks ✪ *Sheila Broun*

MYRRH (Commiphora Myrrha)

Myrrh is the resin of a tropical tree. It has a long tradition as an offertory herb. Originally used in Egypt and the East, its use spread to Europe with travelers, traders and immigrants. Myrrh increases the ritual power of any herb it is burned with. As we burn our herbs and offer prayers, the smoke becomes a tangible symbol of matter joining with Spirit to create magic. Associated with Venus, Artemis, Aphrodite, Astarte and Marian.

© Colette Gardiner 1992

♐ 🌓 sabado
10

♂ ☍ ♅	0:23 am
☽ ✳ ♃	0:42 am
☉ ◻ ♆	4:56 pm
☉ △ ☽	11:42 pm

♐
♑ 🌓 domingo
11

☽ ◻ ♅	5:37 am
☽ ✳ ♄	10:59 am
☿ △ ♀	12:16 pm	☽ v/c
☽ → ♑	3:24 pm
☉ ◻ ♅	5:11 pm

April

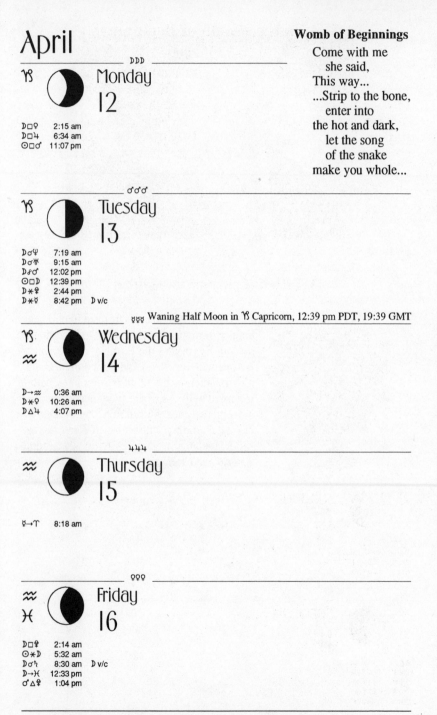

♌)))

♑ **Monday**
12

☽□♀   2:15 am
☽□♃   6:34 am
☉□♂ 11:07 pm

♂♂♂

♑ **Tuesday**
13

☽♂♆   7:19 am
☽♂♅   9:15 am
☽☌♂ 12:02 pm
☉□☽ 12:39 pm
☽✶♀   2:44 pm
☽✶♇   8:42 pm   ☽ v/c

☿☿☿ Waning Half Moon in ♑ Capricorn, 12:39 pm PDT, 19:39 GMT

♑
♒ **Wednesday**
14

☽→♒   0:36 am
☽✶♀ 10:26 am
☽△♃   4:07 pm

♃♃♃

♒ **Thursday**
15

☿→♈   8:18 am

♀♀♀

♒
♓ **Friday**
16

☽□♀   2:14 am
☉✶☽   5:32 am
☽☌♄   8:30 am   ☽ v/c
☽→♓ 12:33 pm
♂△♀   1:04 pm

All aspects in Pacific Daylight Time; add 3 hours for EDT; add 7 hours for GMT

Within the Womb of Beginnings
(Sweat Lodge)

...The smell of herbs;
   eucalyptus and sage
permeate my senses
   as they drift out
from the small,
canvas opening.

The cold air
   bites my breasts,
I crouch low
   and crawl like a caterpillar
awaiting metamorphosis
   in this steaming cocoon...

...She sprinkles water
   on the red rocks
and they hiss and spit
   their primordial snake song.
Holding a leaf of sage
   to the hot embers
she ignites the herb
   and as the vapor smoke rises
she chants; "O Mtakahasi"
   blessing the four directions
with an owl feather.

She is the Mother
   of this hot, dark womb,
we are the seeds
   awaiting new birth.
Cast back to our beginnings
   beholding the infinite circle
the circle that connects us
   to the center of creation...

...We crouch on all fours
   crawling like our animal totems
and one by one,
   we slip through
the small canvas opening
   into a cold, new darkness.

Still slippery with sweat,
   I feel like I'm covered
with the blood of labor,
   I'm born again
like I have been born
   1,000 times before.

✿ *Rosemary Denys Sheola*

♓ 🌓 Saturday 17

☉✶♄ 8:39 pm
☽ApG 10:04 pm

♓ 🌓 Sunday 18

♀☌♀ 5:28 am
☽✶♆ 7:22 am
☽✶♅ 9:26 am
☽△♃ 2:49 pm
☽△♂ 4:51 pm ☽ v/c

To Aphrodite:
A Woman's Invocation

We, Womyn, have called You Goddess
   and blessed Your name, Aphrodite,
      Goddess of "love" and "beauty",
      and we who felt not beautiful,
      wept because we believed ourselves
        unbeautiful and unloved....

...We have seen You as the perfect Woman/Goddess
      none of us could ever be.

Still, You are the Goddess,
      and the Goddess is each of us:
So we, now and for all time to come,
    Invoke You, Aphrodite
    with our full hearts,
      As the Goddess in ourselves,
      the beauty in each of us,
      the desirable woman in each of us,
      the loving woman in each of us.
We reclaim You as part of each woman,
And welcome You into our Circle of Love.
      So mote it Be.

edited excerpts, Ierdeth n'ha Adele
© *Patricia MacAodha 9988/1988*

Venus of Willendorf
and Christopher
(self portrait)
✪ *P.L. Zukas 1991*

V. EARTH LOVING MOON

may we embody the spirit of love

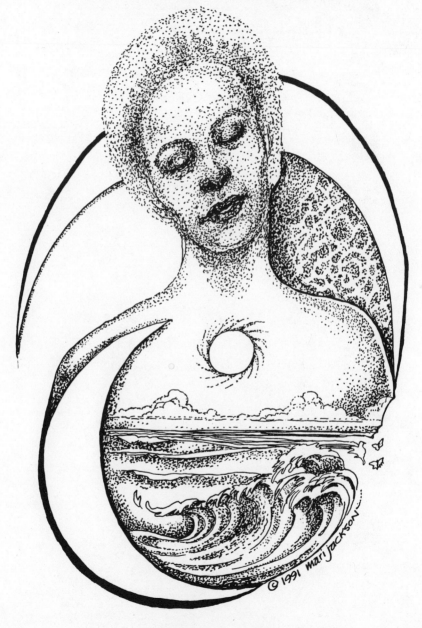

April

♓
♈  ⊃⊃⊃ **Montag**
19

☽→♈	1:15 am
☽☌♀	9:07 am
☽☌♉	1:24 pm
☽☍♃	3:54 pm
☉→♉	6:50 pm

Sun in Taurus, 6:50 pm PDT

1:50 GMT

♈ ♂♂♂ **Dienstag**
20

♉☍♃	8:00 am
☽□♆	7:37 pm
☽□♅	9:39 pm

♈
♉ ☿☿☿ **Mittwoch**
21

☽□♂	7:15 am	
☽✶♄	9:58 am	☽ v/c
☽→♉	1:08 pm	

New Moon in ♉ Taurus, 4:49 pm PDT, 23:49 GMT

♉ ♃♃♃ **Donnerstag**
22

♀ D	7:12 am
♆ ℞	10:01 am

♉
♊ ♀♀♀ **Freitag**
23

☉☌☽	4:49 pm	
☽△♆	6:27 am	
☽△♅	8:27 am	
☽☍♀	1:18 pm	
☽✶♂	7:58 pm	
☽□♄	8:43 pm	☽ v/c

All aspects in Pacific Daylight Time; add 3 hours for EDT; add 7 hours for GMT

TAURUS - *Rock*

1992-93 is a doorway, with the Uranus/Neptune conjunction shattering and dissolving enough of our rigid mindset to allow for a new way of thinking to emerge. Taurus responds as an earth sign, attempting to translate these startling perceptions into everyday life. New ideas and concepts are brought into your field of work; progressive views on education and uncanny insights into the future reflect this open and impressionable stage of growth. You are likely to be teaching, sharing your techniques and perceptions. New horizons, new perspectives may occasionally blur your viewpoint, making it hard to know in what direction to move.

There are clues to handling such wild times: stay as flexible and open-minded as you, dear Taurus, can manage. When you seize up and begin to resist and retreat into your own private view of life, circumstances will arise to drag you back out into the fray. Travel and/or contact with people from other cultures will provide insights. Refine your skills; take care of your health.

With Saturn in your solar 10th house, 1991-93 is time to harvest your efforts of the last 20-24 years. If you are ever to be a leader, it is now. However, there are a number of pitfalls to this period. Do not take shortcuts to power, or protect those who are in error. Admit mistakes. What is covered up is likely to surface. Do not become so focused upon external affairs that you overlook what is going on in your personal life.

Saturn square Pluto forms a tense t-square in your chart this year; relationships continue to be catalysts for personal growth, plunging you into your shadows. Breakdowns occur; each person is freed to grow separately, or perhaps you experience a series of mini deaths and rebirths within the relationship.

© *Gretchen Lawlor 1992*

♉ ☿
♊

Samstag
24

D→♊   11:27 pm
D☀♀   6:44 am

♊

Sonntag
25

D△♃   12:21 pm
D☀♅   3:40 am

© *Patricia Levey 1986*

avril

☽☽☽

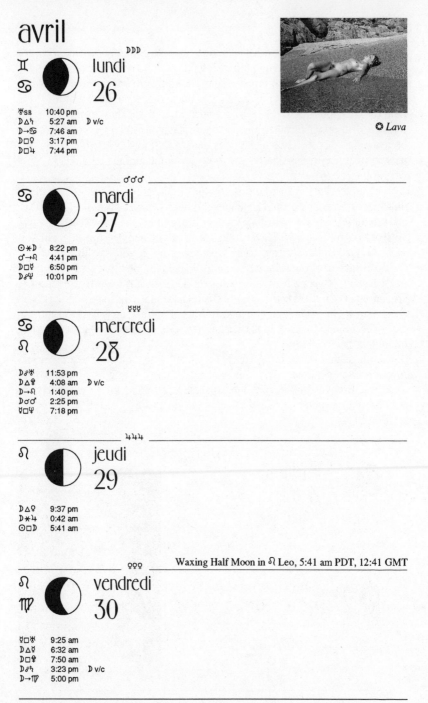

♊ ♋ lundi 26

✪ *Lava*

♅SR 10:40 pm
☽△♄ 5:27 am ☽ v/c
☽→♋ 7:46 am
☽□♀ 3:17 pm
☽□♃ 7:44 pm

♂♂♂

♋ mardi 27

☉✶☽ 8:22 pm
♂→♌ 4:41 pm
☽□☿ 6:50 pm
☽☍♆ 10:01 pm

☿☿☿

♋ ♌ mercredi 28

☽☍♅ 11:53 pm
☽△♇ 4:08 am ☽ v/c
☽→♌ 1:40 pm
☽☌♂ 2:25 pm
☿□♆ 7:18 pm

♃♃♃

♌ jeudi 29

☽△♀ 9:37 pm
☽✶♃ 0:42 am
☉□☽ 5:41 am

Waxing Half Moon in ♌ Leo, 5:41 am PDT, 12:41 GMT

♀♀♀

♌ ♍ vendredi 30

☿□♅ 9:25 am
☽△☿ 6:32 am
☽□♇ 7:50 am
☽☍♄ 3:23 pm ☽ v/c
☽→♍ 5:00 pm

All aspects in Pacific Daylight Time; add 3 hours for EDT; add 7 hours for GMT

The Lesbian Mind, Metaphors II ☯ *Judy Springer 1988*

Weeping for Joy

Come, lay your skin on mine. Bring your skin—somewhere out there listening—back to your self, then lay it on mine. They'll discover us, our skins, vulnerabilities thinly whispering, and when they're done making sure, kissing us hungrily. Come to me then with all your ties, with your skin flowing behind you like a bridal train. Come to me with all your daughters, and we'll arrange the beds border to border, like a rolling landscape, endlessly unfolding, like a woman's body unfolding, waist, then bony hip, then her down-soft inner thigh, weeping for joy.

☯ *Janine Canan*

Beltane Song

Sappha Rauni Bona Dea
Flora   Vesta Aphrodite
Danu   Maia   Seronia

Come Lady May to Beltane fires
Where maidenearth so ripe is waiting
Dance the music of your desires
Jump the flames, toss the flowers
Search out honey-scented bowers
Find the altar to the maiden
Drink her nectar, taste her bread
Lay her down on earth's warm bed
Light more fires, jump more flames
Come Lady May to Beltane games

Sappha Rauni Bona Dea
Flora   Vesta Aphrodite
Danu   Maia   Seronia

© *Ila Suzanne 1986*

Beltane *is the midpoint between Spring Equinox and Summer Solstice. This is one of the four ancient fire festivals of Europe, also called the "Power Gates", which contain the fixed zodiacal signs. The sign of Beltane is the Power Gate of the Earth element.* ***Theme: Passion.***

excerpt from Wild Witches Don't Get The Blues © *Ffiona Morgan 1991*

© Anne Hendahl-Owen

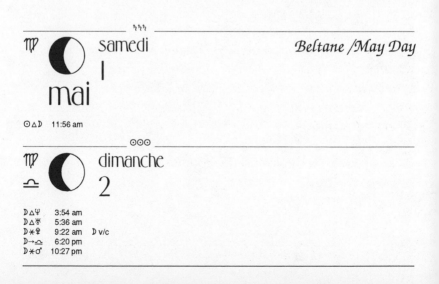

♍ 🌓 samedi
1
mai

Beltane /May Day

☉△☽ 11:56 am

♍ 🌓 dimanche
♎ 2

☽△♆ 3:54 am
☽△♅ 5:36 am
☽⚹♀ 9:22 am ☽ v/c
☽→♎ 6:20 pm
☽⚹♂ 10:27 pm

mayo

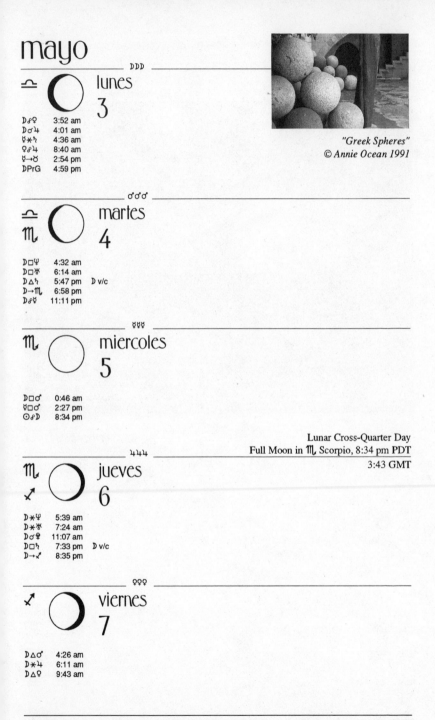

DDD ──────────

♎ 🌑 **lunes**
3

☽☌♀	3:52 am
☽☌♃	4:01 am
☿⚹♄	4:36 am
♀☌♃	8:40 am
☿→♉	2:54 pm
☽PrG	4:59 pm

"Greek Spheres"
© Annie Ocean 1991

♂♂♂ ──────────

♎
♏ 🌘 **martes**
4

☽□♆	4:32 am	
☽□♅	6:14 am	
☽△♄	5:47 pm	☽ v/c
☽→♏	6:58 pm	
☽☌♉	11:11 pm	

☿☿☿ ──────────

♏ 🌑 **miercoles**
5

☽□♂	0:46 am
☿□♂	2:27 pm
☉☍☽	8:34 pm

Lunar Cross-Quarter Day
Full Moon in ♏ Scorpio, 8:34 pm PDT
3:43 GMT

♃♃♃ ──────────

♏
♐ 🌘 **jueves**
6

☽⚹♆	5:39 am	
☽⚹♅	7:24 am	
☽☌♀	11:07 am	
☽□♄	7:33 pm	☽ v/c
☽→♐	8:35 pm	

♀♀♀ ──────────

♐ 🌘 **viernes**
7

☽△♂	4:26 am
☽⚹♃	6:11 am
☽△♀	9:43 am

──

All aspects except April 6 in Pacific Daylight Time; add 3 hours for EDT; add 7 hours for GMT

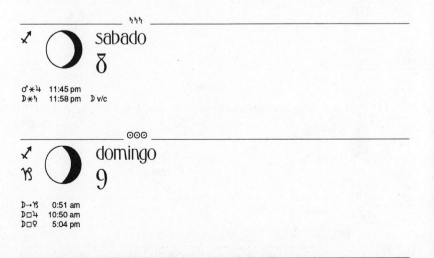

Carina King

♐ 🌒 **sabado**
  ♉

♂✶♃ 11:45 pm
☽✶♄ 11:58 pm   ☽ v/c

⊙⊙⊙

♐ 🌓 **domingo**
♑   **9**

☽→♑   0:51 am
☽□♃ 10:50 am
☽□♀   5:04 pm

May

DDD

♑ 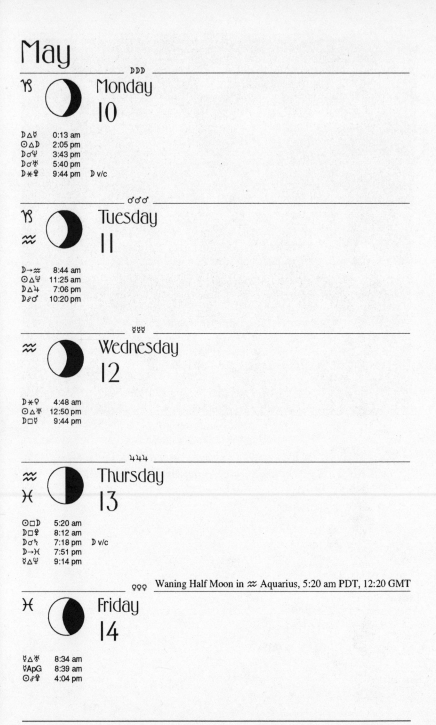 **Monday**
10

D △ ♅ 0:13 am
⊙ △ D 2:05 pm
D ♂ Ψ 3:43 pm
D ♂ ♅ 5:40 pm
D ✳ ♀ 9:44 pm D v/c

♂♂♂

♑
≈ **Tuesday**
11

D → ≈ 8:44 am
⊙ △ Ψ 11:25 am
D △ ♃ 7:06 pm
D ♂ ♂ 10:20 pm

☿☿☿

≈ **Wednesday**
12

D ✳ ♀ 4:48 am
⊙ △ ♅ 12:50 pm
D □ ☿ 9:44 pm

♃♃♃

≈
♓ **Thursday**
13

⊙ □ D 5:20 am
D □ ♀ 8:12 am
D ♂ ♄ 7:18 pm D v/c
D → ♓ 7:51 pm
☿ △ Ψ 9:14 pm

♀♀♀ Waning Half Moon in ≈ Aquarius, 5:20 am PDT, 12:20 GMT

♓ **Friday**
14

☿ △ ♅ 8:34 am
☿ApG 8:39 am
⊙ ♂ ♀ 4:04 pm

All aspects in Pacific Daylight Time; add 3 hours for EDT; add 7 hours for GMT

Hug © *Shoshana Rothaizer 1983*

ROSE (Rosa spp)

The rose, with its sweet smell and floral beauty, has long been a symbol of love. Use the petals of unsprayed roses in baths to bring out your loving and sacred nature. Very soothing to the skin and the body when eaten. Try using small unsprayed petals in fruit salad, punch or tea. Sacred to Demeter, Aurora, Venus and Aphrodite.

© *Colette Gardiner 1992*

♓ 🌓 **Saturday 15**

♀PrG	0:47 am	⊙♂♉	7:51 pm	
♉♂♀	7:22 am	☽△♀	8:30 pm	
☽✶♆	2:15 pm	⊙✶☽	11:06 pm	
☽ApG	2:54 pm	☽✶♉	11:30 pm	☽ v/c
☽✶♅	4:19 pm			

○○○

♓ ♈ 🌓 **Sunday 16**

☽→♈	8:25 am
☽☍♃	6:41 pm
☽△♂	3:58 am

mai

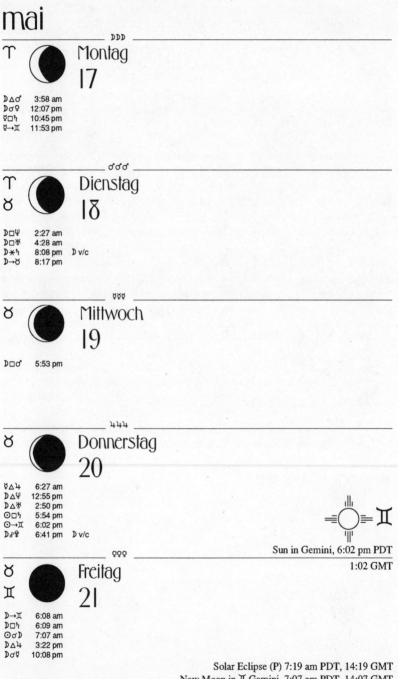

ↀↀↀ

♈ **Montag**
17

☽△♂	3:58 am
☽♂♀	12:07 pm
☿□♄	10:45 pm
☿→♊	11:53 pm

♂♂♂

♈
♉ **Dienstag**
18

☽□♆	2:27 am
☽□♅	4:28 am
☽⚹♄	8:08 pm ☽ v/c
☽→♉	8:17 pm

☿☿☿

♉ **Mittwoch**
19

☽□♂	5:53 pm

♃♃♃

♉ **Donnerstag**
20

☿△♃	6:27 am
☽△♆	12:55 pm
☽△♅	2:50 pm
☉□♄	5:54 pm
☉→♊	6:02 pm
☽☍♀	6:41 pm ☽ v/c

Sun in Gemini, 6:02 pm PDT
1:02 GMT

♀♀♀

♉
♊ **Freitag**
21

☽→♊	6:08 am
☽□♄	6:09 am
☉♂☽	7:07 am
☽△♃	3:22 pm
☽♂♉	10:08 pm

Solar Eclipse (P) 7:19 am PDT, 14:19 GMT
New Moon in ♊ Gemini, 7:07 am PDT, 14:07 GMT

All aspects in Pacific Daylight Time; add 3 hours for EDT; add 7 hours for GMT

GEMINI - *Breeze* (MAY 20—JUNE 20)

Gemini is in a time of mindshift; '92-'93 will accentuate your openness and resiliency, the power of surrender. Use your body, especially your nervous system, as your barometer. If body complains, you are taking in too much.

Saturn in Aquarius ('91-'93) assists your explorations with a framework within which to wander—whether it be a clear philosophy, a meaningful and tangible goal to aspire to, or a course of study. You are preparing for a time of leadership ('93-'95) and need to get your parameters, your philosophical framework in place now. Gemini easily becomes overwhelmed with indiscriminate learning/understanding; you need limits, boundaries and clear goals to set your course on. Already you are influencing others—through teaching, lecturing and spreading the word.

With Jupiter transiting your house of creativity and play, you are experiencing a burst of productivity, finding courage to express yourself without doubts. You no longer feel it necessary to hide from the world. Love affairs open you up to life, exploring sexual and sacred realms with curiosity and experimentation.

The potent Uranus/Neptune conjunction is/has been bringing about sudden unexpected shifts in your life, of a peculiarly intense and fateful quality. An old order passes; a new one comes on, seemingly overnight. You receive guidance and inspiration through meditation and dreams. You are able to tap into expanded vision and understanding, outpouring this best through art, children and playfulness within a philosophical/religious/spiritual framework.

You are able to serve as a source of comfort and inspiration for others experiencing crisis. However, your psychic openness can be experienced in less desirable ways too—you may feel overwhelmed by what you are picking up. Your physical handicaps (especially your nerves), will require you to establish boundaries, to eliminate unnecessary input. Friends and group support systems help you to protect yourself.

© *Gretchen Lawlor 1992*

ↄↄↄ

♊ ● Samstag
22

☽⚹♂ 5:18 am
☽⚹♀ 2:54 pm   ☽ v/c

☉☉☉

♊ ● Sonntag
♋ 23

☽→♋ 1:38 pm
☽△♄ 1:47 pm
☽□♃ 10:25 pm

"Shamanflight" © *Minerva 1991*

Invocation

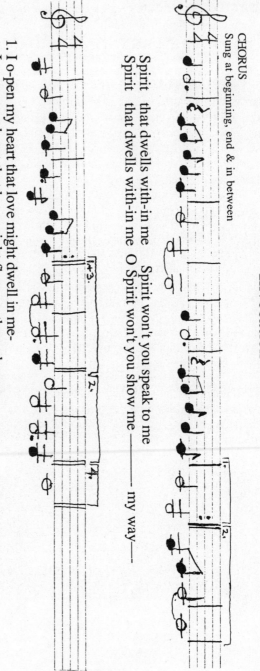

Spirit   that dwells with-in me   Spirit won't you speak to me
Spirit   that dwells with-in me   O Spirit won't you show me —————— my way ——

1. I o-pen my heart that love might dwell in me-
   I o-pen my heart that love might flow—— through me-
   I o-pen my heart that love might flow from me-
   I o-pen my heart that love might ———— grow.

2. I o-pen my eyes that I might see you
   I o-pen my ears that I might——— ——- hear you
   I o-pen my mouth that I might speak of you
   I o-pen myself unto ————————-you.

Joys Dancer

VI. MOON OF MUSES
inspire us with divine creativity

mai

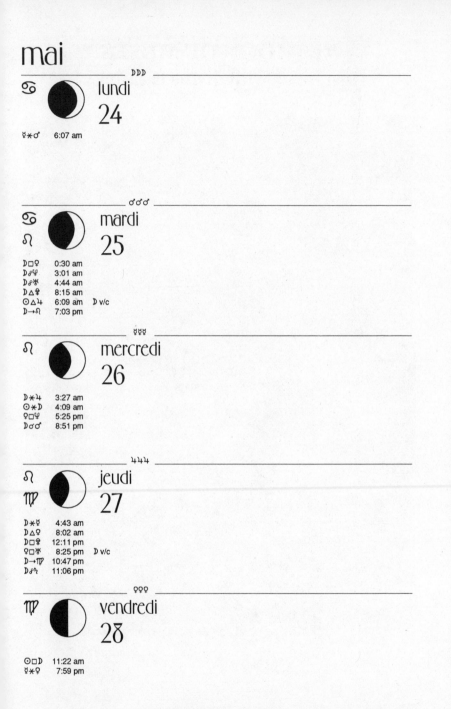

♋ **lundi 24** ⟩⟩⟩

☿⚹♂ 6:07 am

♋ ♌ **mardi 25** ♂♂♂

☽□♀ 0:30 am
☽☌♆ 3:01 am
☽☌♅ 4:44 am
☽△♀ 8:15 am
☉△♃ 6:09 am ☽ v/c
☽→♌ 7:03 pm

♌ **mercredi 26** ☿☿☿

☽⚹♃ 3:27 am
☉⚹☽ 4:09 am
♀□♆ 5:25 pm
☽☌♂ 8:51 pm

♌ ♍ **jeudi 27** ♃♃♃

☽⚹♀ 4:43 am
☽△♀ 8:02 am
☽□♀ 12:11 pm
♀□♅ 8:25 pm ☽ v/c
☽→♍ 10:47 pm
☽☌♄ 11:06 pm

♍ **vendredi 28** ♀♀♀

☉□☽ 11:22 am
☿⚹♀ 7:59 pm

Waxing Half Moon in ♍ Virgo, 11:22 am PDT, 18:22 GMT

All aspects in Pacific Daylight Time; add 3 hours for EDT; add 7 hours for GMT

Carolyn McTaggart

Third Sister

My loom hums
to dress the new world.
The porch smells from children's wings.
What is it I trade each night
for feather pillows?
What do I lose to science in the morning?

excerpt from "As If Dedalus Were The Hero"
✪ *Marcia Cohee*

♍ 🌔 samedi
29

☽△♆ 9:55 am
☽△♅ 11:30 am
☽✶♀ 2:49 pm
☽□♅ 3:33 pm   ☽ v/c

♍ 🌗 dimanche
♎   30

☽→♎ 1:18 am
☽♂♃ 9:16 am
☉△☽ 5:18 pm
☽PrG 4:10 am

mayo

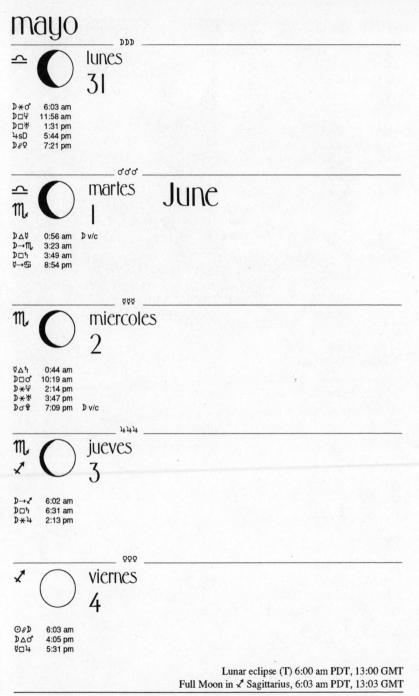

♌♌♌

≏ **lunes**
31

☽⚹♂	6:03 am
☽□♆	11:58 am
☽□♅	1:31 pm
♃sD	5:44 pm
☽☍♀	7:21 pm

♂♂♂

≏
♏ **martes**
1

June

☽△♅	0:56 am	☽ v/c
☽→♏	3:23 am
☽□♄	3:49 am
♅→♋	8:54 pm

☿☿☿

♏ **miercoles**
2

☿△♄	0:44 am
☽□♂	10:19 am
☽⚹♆	2:14 pm
☽⚹♅	3:47 pm
☽☌♀	7:09 pm	☽ v/c

♃♃♃

♏
♐ **jueves**
3

☽→♐	6:02 am
☽□♄	6:31 am
☽⚹♃	2:13 pm

♀♀♀

♐ **viernes**
4

☉☍☽	6:03 am
☽△♂	4:05 pm
☿□♃	5:31 pm

Lunar eclipse (T) 6:00 am PDT, 13:00 GMT
Full Moon in ♐ Sagittarius, 6:03 am PDT, 13:03 GMT

All aspects in Pacific Daylight Time; add 3 hours for EDT; add 7 hours for GMT

MINT (Mentha spp.)

As we start to use our creative selves to express our passion, it is good to have allies that help support our mental energies. In ritual and on the physical plane, mint has a stimulating and clearing effect on the brain. The freshly crushed leaves are invigorating, as is a cup of tea. Try chewing a fresh sprig of mint when you need a "break." Mint is associated with all water spirits, undines, etc., and to a lesser degree with Hecate.

© Colette Gardiner 1992

The Weaver   © Carolyn Hillyer 1991

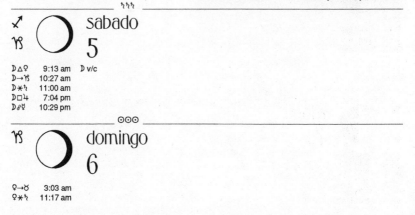

| ♐ ☽ | | sabado |
| ♑ | | 5 |

☽△♀ 9:13 am   ☽ v/c
☽→♑ 10:27 am
☽✳♄ 11:00 am
☽□♃ 7:04 pm
☽♂♅ 10:29 pm

| ♑ ☽ | | domingo |
| | | 6 |

♀→♉ 3:03 am
♀✳♄ 11:17 am

June

♑
♒ 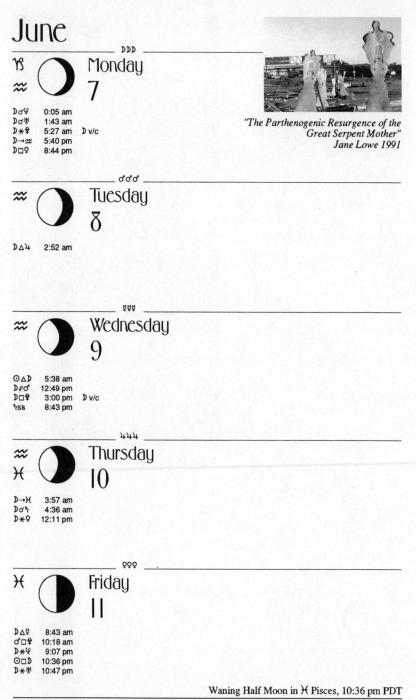 ## Monday
7

☽☌♆	0:05 am	
☽☌♅	1:43 am	
☽✶♀	5:27 am	☽ v/c
☽→♒	5:40 pm	
☽□♀	8:44 pm	

"The Parthenogenic Resurgence of the
Great Serpent Mother"
Jane Lowe 1991

♒ ## Tuesday
8

☽△♃	2:52 am

♒ ## Wednesday
9

☉△☽	5:38 am	
☽☍♂	12:49 pm	
☽□♀	3:00 pm	☽ v/c
♄SR	8:43 pm	

♒
♓ ## Thursday
10

☽→♓	3:57 am
☽☌♄	4:36 am
☽✶♀	12:11 pm

♓ ## Friday
11

☽△☿	8:43 am
♂□♀	10:18 am
☽✶♆	9:07 pm
☉□☽	10:36 pm
☽✶♅	10:47 pm

Waning Half Moon in ♓ Pisces, 10:36 pm PDT

All aspects in Pacific Daylight Time; add 3 hours for EDT; add 7 hours for GMT

The Reemergence of the Great Serpent Mother

15 feet tall, copper, plywood, steel; erected May 1991 on UC Berkeley campus where she stayed for one week of worship and adoration. She was then moved to the Emeryville mud flats where she penetrated the consciousness of commuters and the mainstream media. One week later a man was seen destroying Her with a pick axe. 13 days later we put up 13 cardboard replicas 5'-12' tall: "The Parthenogenic Resurgence of the Great Serpent Mother", (above left). Eventually, the Oakland Tribune ran an editorial endorsing Goddess worship. Blessed be.

Theomophoria
Jane Lowe 1991

The inscription on the sculpture read:

Who is she? Based on figurines found on Crete, 2500-1500 B.C.E. she is the goddess of birth, life, death, underworld, rebirth, prophesy, destiny, sensuality, sex, pleasure, ecstasy, power, omniscience and fertility. Her culture was one of peace, good plumbing and fluid art. A good time was had by all.   *Jane Lowe 1991*

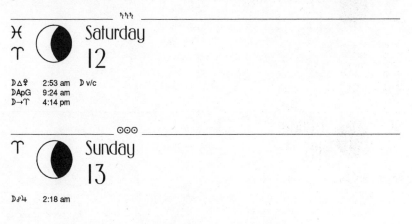

♓
♈
Saturday
12

☽△♀ 2:53 am ☽ v/c
☽ApG 9:24 am
☽→♈ 4:14 pm

♈
Sunday
13

☽☍♃ 2:18 am

Juni

♈ Montag
14

☽□☿	4:02 am
☽□♆	9:25 am
☽□♅	11:00 am
☉⚹☽	4:12 pm
☽△♂	7:01 pm ☽ v/c

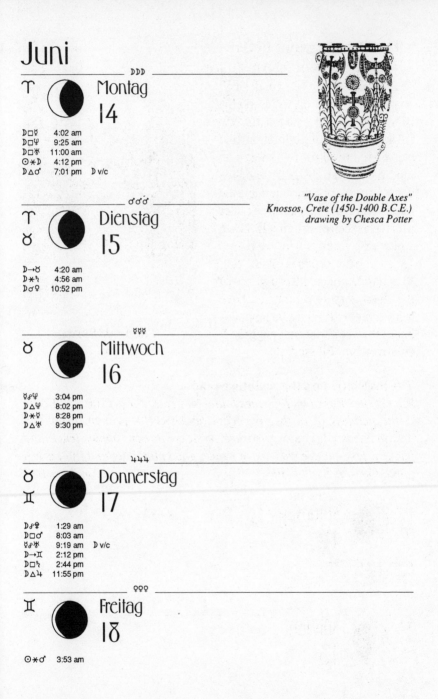

"Vase of the Double Axes"
Knossos, Crete (1450-1400 B.C.E.)
drawing by Chesca Potter

♂♂♂

♈
♉ Dienstag
15

☽→♉	4:20 am
☽⚹♄	4:56 am
☽♂♀	10:52 pm

☿☿☿

♉ Mittwoch
16

☿☍♆	3:04 pm
☽△♆	8:02 pm
☽⚹☿	8:28 pm
☽△♅	9:30 pm

♃♃♃

♉
♊ Donnerstag
17

☽☍♀	1:29 am
☽□♂	8:03 am
☿☍♅	9:19 am ☽ v/c
☽→♊	2:12 pm
☽□♄	2:44 pm
☽△♃	11:55 pm

♀♀♀

♊ Freitag
18

☉⚹♂	3:53 am

All aspects in Pacific Daylight Time; add 3 hours for EDT; add 7 hours for GMT

The Horned One © *Lori Moon Nicolosi*

Mother of Earth, Sea and Air

Mother of Sweetness.
Pearlike, painful, vibrant,
I collect your voices,
the number of completion
I am
in love with your works
I seek to recreate them,
alive to sustain
your oneness.

Anne Kirby McCarthy

♑♑♑

♊
♋

Samstag
19

☿△♀	4:14 pm	
☽✶♂	5:43 pm	
☉♂☽	6:53 pm	☽ v/c
☽→♋	9:05 pm	
☽△♄	9:32 pm	

☉☉☉

New Moon in ♊ Gemini, 6:53 pm PDT

1:53 GMT

♋

Sonntag
20

☽□♃	6:32 am
☽✶♀	10:37 pm

Crimson Blood Wheel

I bleed in the East.
Place of illumination.
Warm yellow glow of morning,
Where I feel the gentleness of new
        beginnings.

I bleed in the South.
Where my heart opens to the trickster.
Where humor and acceptance yield
blessings,
        kisses.
Sacred season of summer.

I bleed in the West.
Where the dancing black bear dwells.
Where introspection is a gateway to the
        secrets.
Death, rebirth and change are welcomed
        friends.

I bleed in the North.
Wisdom fire of knowledge.
Where buffalo lands criss-cross
Mother's breasts.
Images of worship, spiritual power and
        the serpent rising inside.

✪ *Gentle Doe*

VII. FLOWING MOON
let us feel our oneness with you

juin

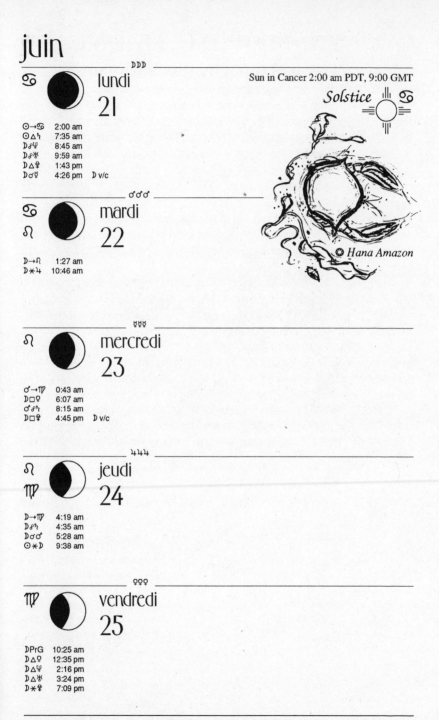

ⅅⅅⅅ

♋ **lundi**
21

Sun in Cancer 2:00 am PDT, 9:00 GMT

Solstice ♋

☉→♋ 2:00 am
☉△♄ 7:35 am
☽☍♆ 8:45 am
☽☍♅ 9:59 am
☽△♀ 1:43 pm
☽♂♂ 4:26 pm ☽ v/c

♂♂♂

♋
♌ **mardi**
22

☽→♌ 1:27 am
☽✳♃ 10:46 am

☿☿☿

♌ **mercredi**
23

♂→♍ 0:43 am
☽□♀ 6:07 am
♂☍♄ 8:15 am
☽□♀ 4:45 pm ☽ v/c

♃♃♃

♌
♍ **jeudi**
24

☽→♍ 4:19 am
☽☍♄ 4:35 am
☽♂♂ 5:28 am
☉✳☽ 9:38 am

♀♀♀

♍ **vendredi**
25

☽PrG 10:25 am
☽△♀ 12:35 pm
☽△♆ 2:16 pm
☽△♅ 3:24 pm
☽✳♀ 7:09 pm

© Hana Amazon

All aspects in Pacific Daylight Time; add 3 hours for EDT; add 7 hours for GMT

Unexpected or inspiring experiences with others (love or hate, association or conflict) throw your whole life into chaos in the early '90's.

Saturn always indicates areas requiring attention—in '92 and '93 it is your fear of letting go, of intimacy, even of joint resources, that needs work. Uranus/Neptune powerfully conjuncting in your house of relationships challenge you to accept big changes in the way you relate to people on a one-to-one basis.

You project creativity and vitality, (as well as instability, irresponsibility) onto other people, rather than seeing it in yourself, or in your existing relationships. A basically solid relationship will weather these storms as long as you both are able to embrace big changes in each other and in the purpose and form of the relationship. Old relationships that have served their purpose, or cannot accommodate this rapid growth will end so healthier ones can emerge.

There have been urges for change rising in you for years—this conjunction only hastens the rhythm of experience. The energy that has been building over the issue of freedom and creativity in relationships has become a formidable reservoir of tension and is to be confronted now.

Formidable times—what helps? Put down roots, have a sense of belonging to a place, a community and family. Have faith that there is a tremendous capacity for transformation in you right now, that old emotional knots can be exorcised if you are willing to face them. Some fear or insecurity from your childhood is inhibiting—look for help (counseling, therapy) to exorcise it.

By the end of '93 you will feel more able to find the wild creative spirit within yourself. A lighter, sunnier presence is waking in you demanding to be let out to play.

© *Gretchen Lawlor 1992*

♍︎ ☽ **samedi**
♎︎ **26**

☽✱♅ 2:02 am   ☽ v/c
☽→♎︎ 6:46 am
♀△♅ 11:11 am
☉□☽ 3:44 pm
☽♂♃ 4:27 pm

♎︎ ☽ **dimanche**
27

♀△♅ 1:47 am
☉□♃ 3:11 am
☽□♆ 4:50 pm
☽□♅ 5:56 pm

Waxing Half Moon in ♎︎ Libra, 3:44 pm PDT, 22:44 GMT

Summer Solstice

Sing and spin, sing and spin
Half year out, half year in
Earth at full must spiral in
Summer solstice longest light
Burn all fears this brief night
Fairy wheels now start again
Sing and spin, sing and spin

© *Ila Suzanne 1986*

junio

I celebrate my roundness—
found in my Capricorn moon.
I celebrate my freedom,
to release my subtle gloom...
excerpt ☉ Amikaeyla

〉〉〉

♎︎
♏︎   ◐   **lunes**
         28

☽□♀	6:01 am	☽ v/c
☽→♏︎	9:38 am	
☽△♄	9:43 am	
☽✳︎♂	3:11 pm	
☉△☽	10:28 pm	

♂♂♂

♏︎   ◑   **martes**
         29

♀☍♇	4:35 am
☽✳︎♅	8:12 pm
☽✳︎♆	9:16 pm

☿☿☿

♏︎
♐︎   ◑   **miercoles**
         30

☽☌♀	1:18 am	
☽☍♀	3:02 am	
☽△♀	10:22 am	
☽□♄	1:27 pm	☽ v/c
☽→♐︎	1:28 pm	
☽□♂	9:29 pm	

♃♃♃

♐︎   ◯   **jueves**
         1

julio

| ☽✳︎♃ | 0:09 am |

♀♀♀

♐︎
♑︎   ◯   **viernes**
         2

| ☽✳︎♄ | 6:39 pm | ☽ v/c |
| ☽→♑︎ | 6:49 pm | |

All aspects in Pacific Daylight Time; add 3 hours for EDT; add 7 hours for GMT

© C. McGuire

♄♄♄

♑ ◯ sabado
3

☽△♂ 5:36 am
☽□♃ 6:14 am
☉☍☽ 4:46 pm
☿⚹♀ 8:59 pm

☉☉☉ Full Moon in ♑ Capricorn, 4:46 pm PDT, 23:46 GMT

♑ ◑ domingo
4

☽☌♆ 7:27 am
☽☌♅ 8:29 am
☽⚹♀ 1:00 pm
☽☍♂ 10:03 pm

July

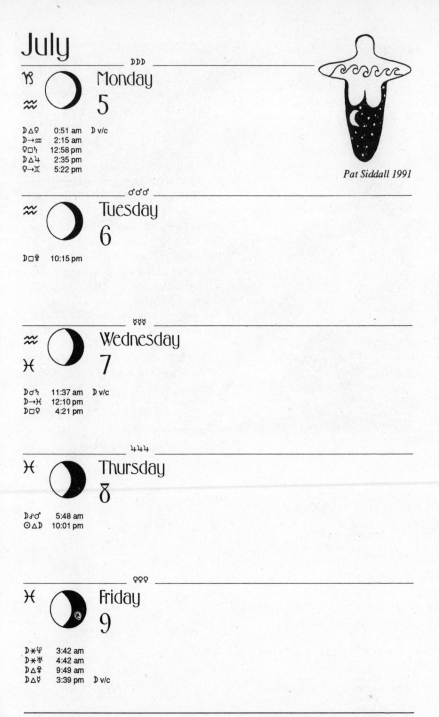

♑ ☽ ☽☽☽ **Monday**
♒ **5**

☽△♀ 0:51 am ☽ v/c
☽→♒ 2:15 am
♀□♄ 12:58 pm
☽△♃ 2:35 pm
♀→♊ 5:22 pm

Pat Siddall 1991

♒ ☽ ♂♂♂ **Tuesday**
6

☽□♀ 10:15 pm

♒ ☽ ☿☿☿ **Wednesday**
♓ **7**

☽♂♄ 11:37 am ☽ v/c
☽→♓ 12:10 pm
☽□♀ 4:21 pm

♓ ☽ ♃♃♃ **Thursday**
8

☽♂♂ 5:48 am
☉△☽ 10:01 pm

♓ ☽ ♀♀♀ **Friday**
9

☽✶♆ 3:42 am
☽✶♅ 4:42 am
☽△♀ 9:49 am
☽△♅ 3:39 pm ☽ v/c

All aspects in Pacific Daylight Time; add 3 hours for EDT; add 7 hours for GMT

PASSION FLOWER
(Passiflora incarnata)

As we work with Spirit in our lives there are times we all need a break, times we need to let feelings flow. Passion flower helps with the aftermath of feelings, blissful or difficult. Place it beneath a pillow to aid in restful sleep. Placed in your house, it calms troubles. It is often used as a tea or tincture premenstrually to soothe nerves. Drink the tea as needed. Sacred to Venus and Aphrodite.

© Colette Gardiner 1992

CHANTING UP THE MOON

Between Grandmother Moon and our
            song, breath rises in sheets
            of mist
We move sensuously, we open our robes,
We are not afraid.

Yes! Now we can, O Women, now we can
            be awake and dance to tell
            about it.

The chant rises—ancient and sacred
            it rises and rises, the moon
            herself rises
And rises until no heart could hang hard
            and heavy in any breast.

We rise to join you, Grandmother Moon,
            lifting our arms, drawing down the
            light, bringing our burdens, our
Joy, our treasure as an offering; it dissolves
            in the mist of our songs, making a
            veil for you, a halo.

We bring our silver breath to you,
            our strong bodies,
            our creative hands raised,
            lifting up our lives
            in praise.

❀ Saya Wolf 1992

♓
♈ ☽ Saturday
         10

☽→♈	0:12 am
☽ApG	3:49 am
☽✳♀	10:32 am
☽☍♃	2:22 pm

♈ ◗ Sunday
        11

♅PrG	2:20 pm
☉□☽	3:49 pm
☽□♆	4:07 pm
☽□♅	5:03 pm
♆PrG	6:28 pm
☉☍♇	7:32 pm
☿PrG	9:05 pm

Waning Half Moon in ♈ Aries, 3:49 pm PDT, 22:49 GMT

Juli

♈
♉
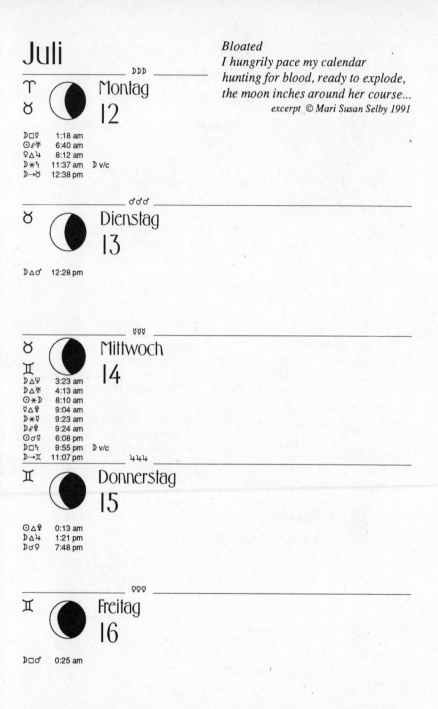

☽☽☽

Montag
12

☽□♅	1:18 am	
☉☍♅	6:40 am	
♀△♃	8:12 am	
☽✶♄	11:37 am	☽ v/c
☽→♉	12:38 pm	

♉

♂♂♂

Dienstag
13

| ☽△♂ | 12:28 pm |

♉
♊

☿☿☿

Mittwoch
14

☽△♆	3:23 am	
☽△♅	4:13 am	
☉✶☽	8:10 am	
☿△♀	9:04 am	
☽✶☿	9:23 am	
☽☍♀	9:24 am	
☉♂☿	6:08 pm	
☽□♄	9:55 pm	☽ v/c
☽→♊	11:07 pm	

♃♃♃

♊

Donnerstag
15

☉△♀	0:13 am
☽△♃	1:21 pm
☽♂♀	7:48 pm

♀♀♀

♊

Freitag
16

| ☽□♂ | 0:25 am |

Traveling Stream

Carry me the length of this traveling stream
Carry me the length of your long gentle smile
Through any signs of trespass
Through any imagined fear of being close, too close
Through your life's rich history.
Take me over the wandering hills and remote passages
Take me with the ideal of summer melting fast
Fast down your lucid throat
Easy to swallow—a taste of ageless fruit...
Float me down the edge of your ocean's roaring wave
Float me over its sparkling surfaced mirror
Drop me in that water and wash me
Let my particles mix with yours, until
I am your vaporous breath and
You are mine.

Jan Larsson

© Judith Burros 1992

♊
♋ | 🌑 | ### Samstag
17

☽△♄   4:48 am   ☽ v/c
☽→♋   6:08 am
☽□♃   7:56 pm

♋ | 🌑 | ### Sonntag
18

☽⚹♂   8:14 am
☽☍♆   4:10 pm
☽☍♅   4:48 pm
☽♂♉   5:09 pm
☽△♀   9:37 pm

Dance Down

Break sound into rainbows
        dance you down dancing
           down
              down

Floorboards   no meadows
I spread out my footprints
        dance you down pagan
           down
              down

Shake echoes and hollow
bones into madness
boldly as shadows
spring lightly spring lightly
        I dance you down dancing
           down
              down

Grace-notes of music
weave circles from drumbeats
the music entices
I follow   I follow
        dance you down dancing
           down
              down

Stars shiver to meaning
Morgana
Astarte
witch-queen and goddess
spin dawn out of dancing
        shake echoes
           weave circles
              dance folly
                dance madness
dance you down dancing
      down
        down

Jennifer Brice

VIII. CELEBRATION MOON
sing out with a joyful heart!

juillet

♌♌♌

♋
♌　⬤　**lundi**
19

♉☍♅　3:36 am
☉☌☽　4:24 am　☽ v/c
☽→♌　9:48 am
♉☍♆　10:31 pm
☽✳♃　11:21 pm

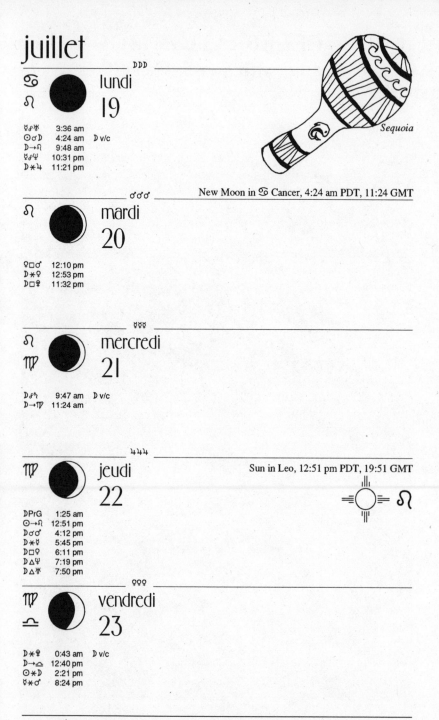

Sequoia

New Moon in ♋ Cancer, 4:24 am PDT, 11:24 GMT

♂♂♂

♌　🌑　**mardi**
20

♀□♂　12:10 pm
☽✳♀　12:53 pm
☽□♀　11:32 pm

☿☿☿

♌
♍　🌑　**mercredi**
21

☽☍♄　9:47 am　☽ v/c
☽→♍　11:24 am

♃♃♃

♍　🌒　**jeudi**
22

Sun in Leo, 12:51 pm PDT, 19:51 GMT

☉ ♌

☽PrG　1:25 am
☉→♌　12:51 pm
☽☌♂　4:12 pm
☽✳♉　5:45 pm
☽□♀　6:11 pm
☽△♆　7:19 pm
☽△♅　7:50 pm

♀♀♀

♍
♎　🌓　**vendredi**
23

☽✳♀　0:43 am　☽ v/c
☽→♎　12:40 pm
☉✳☽　2:21 pm
☿✳♂　8:24 pm

All aspects in Pacific Daylight Time; add 3 hours for EDT; add 7 hours for GMT

LEO - *Flame*

Leo is a vital fiery sign; you've had to moderate that fire considerably in 1992, as Saturn opposed Leo in the house of relationships. This theme continues during 1993 as you are periodically brought crashing down to earth through your relationships. Cooperation is your biggest challenge, as well as your area of greatest potential in '93. It is difficult for Leo to share the stage, but not impossible. You are being asked to do your best, to establish clear guidelines in all relationships, and to live up to your agreements. You are struggling to integrate into your social group, with your individuality still intact.

Jupiter in Libra reinforces this cooperative theme. It is not a time to pit self and ego against the world, but instead to come out of yourself and cooperate with others for mutual progress and protection. Collaborative efforts involving writing, teaching, and travel all benefit in '93. Your mind is exceptionally versatile—you are tolerant, you are frank and willing to say what is on your mind, graciously.

The biggest influence of '93, the conjunction of Uranus/Neptune in Capricorn, hits you in your solar 6th house of health and self discipline. Health problems occurring under this influence are stress related. Illness can provide a chance to escape, to surrender to a more contemplative pace in order to regroup and find meaning for your life.

Work may feel boring, restrictive, without purpose. Neptune ensures that the harder you work for your own benefit, the less you will get out of it. Work has to be for a cause, essentially in service to others. New techniques will come into your mind unexpectedly; it will be hard to be disciplined unless you can tap into some vision of a better future to keep you going.

© *Gretchen Lawlor 1992*

♑︎ 🌓 samedi
24

☽☌♃	3:03 am
☽☐☿	6:58 pm
☽☐♆	9:04 pm
☽☐♅	9:33 pm

♎︎
♏︎ 🌓 dimanche
25

☽△♀	0:16 am	
☽△♄	12:53 pm	☽ v/c
♅sD	1:45 pm	
☽→♏︎	3:01 pm	
♂△♆	3:54 pm	
☉☐☽	8:26 pm	

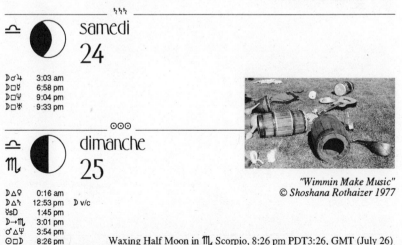

"Wimmin Make Music"
© *Shoshana Rothaizer 1977*

Waxing Half Moon in ♏︎ Scorpio, 8:26 pm PDT3:26, GMT (July 26)

julio

♏ **lunes**
26

♂△♅ 2:14 am
☽△♉ 10:30 pm

🌣 *Kitt Redwing*

♏
♐ **martes**
27

☽⚹♆ 0:28 am
☽⚹♅ 0:56 am
☽⚹♂ 2:04 am
☽☌♀ 6:23 am
☽□♄ 4:46 am ☽ v/c
☽→♐ 7:13 pm

♐ **miercoles**
28

☉△☽ 4:52 am
☽⚹♃ 11:47 am

♐ **jueves**
29

☽□♂ 10:16 am
☽☍♀ 7:30 pm
☽⚹♄ 10:37 pm ☽ v/c

♐
♑ **viernes**
30

☽→♑ 1:27 am
☿☍♆ 7:44 am
☿☍♅ 5:36 pm
☽□♃ 7:15 pm

All aspects in Pacific Daylight Time; add 3 hours for EDT; add 7 hours for GMT

© B. Lynn DiBiase 1991

Grandmother Fire

Grandmother Fire
wind talker ground stalker
Grandmother Fire
to you we sing this song

Grandmother Fire
wind talker ground stalker
Grandmother Fire
make our medicine strong

Light up our lives
center our hearts
and heal these wounds
with your birth

Light up our lives
center our hearts
and warm these bones
from your hearth

Brenwyn

♑ ☾ **sabado**
31

♂✳♀	1:46 am
♀△♄	5:32 am
☽♂♆	1:16 pm
☽♂♅	1:39 pm
☽☍♉	2:39 pm
☽✳♀	7:49 pm
☽△♂	8:44 pm ☽ v/c

◉◉◉

♑ ☾ **domingo**
≈ **1**

☽→≈	9:37 am
♀→♋	3:39 pm
☉✳♃	10:34 pm

agosto

August

DDD

≈ ◯ **Monday**
2

D△♃ 4:44 am
☉♂D 5:10 am
♀D 9:46 am

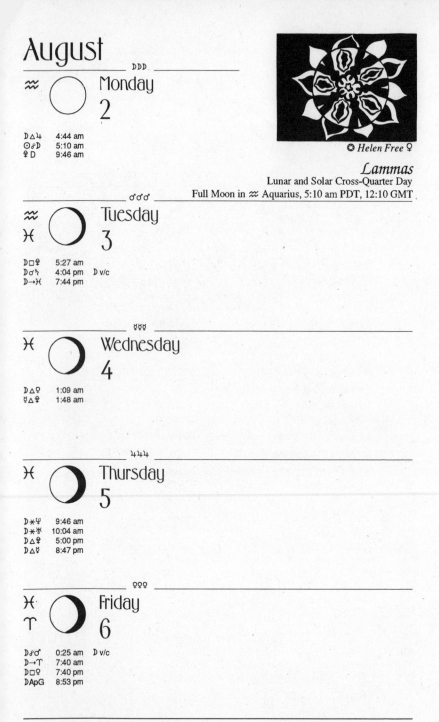

☉ *Helen Free* ♀

Lammas
Lunar and Solar Cross-Quarter Day
Full Moon in ≈ Aquarius, 5:10 am PDT, 12:10 GMT

♂♂♂

≈
⊢ ◖ **Tuesday**
H
3

D□♀ 5:27 am
D♂♄ 4:04 pm   D v/c
D→H 7:44 pm

☿☿☿

H ◖ **Wednesday**
4

D△♀ 1:09 am
☿△♀ 1:48 am

♃♃♃

H ◖ **Thursday**
5

D✶Ψ 9:46 am
D✶♅ 10:04 am
D△♀ 5:00 pm
D△☿ 8:47 pm

♀♀♀

H ◗ **Friday**
♈ 6

D♂♂ 0:25 am   D v/c
D→♈ 7:40 am
D□♀ 7:40 pm
D ApG 8:53 pm

All aspects in Pacific Daylight Time; add 3 hours for EDT; add 7 hours for GMT

Lammas is the mid-point between Summer Solstice and Fall Equinox, a fire festival of the first fruits of Summer's abundance.

Michigan Women's Music Festival   © *Judith Burros 1992*

Electra

Invoking Artemis

From the depths of my soul
I feel her wild, courageous, unstoppable strength
stirring within, urging me to carry on,
against all odds.
She is the power
I once knew, and have to remember,
in regaining what is mine.
I call upon her to guide me
Through this darkness to the light once more.

Mirtha Vega

SAFFRON

As we celebrate the abundance of life it's fun to incorporate special foods and herbs. Saffron was traditionally baked into crescent shaped cookies or cakes to celebrate fertility or invoke lunar energies. One half teaspoon can be added to flour for these cakes. Place them on your altar during a ritual and eat afterwards. Saffron amplifies any healing work. Sacred to Astarte.   *© Colette Gardiner 1992*

ᚺᚺᚺ

♈	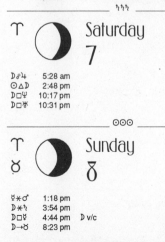	Saturday
		7

☽☍♃	5:28 am	
☉△☽	2:48 pm	
☽□♆	10:17 pm	
☽□♅	10:31 pm	

◎◎◎

♈		Sunday
♉		8

☿⚹♂	1:18 pm	
☽⚹♄	3:54 pm	
☽□♀	4:44 pm	☽ v/c
☽→♉	8:23 pm	

August

ᛜ ♉   ⟩⟩⟩

☽ ## Montag
9

☽⚹♀   2:48 pm
☿→♌   10:51 pm

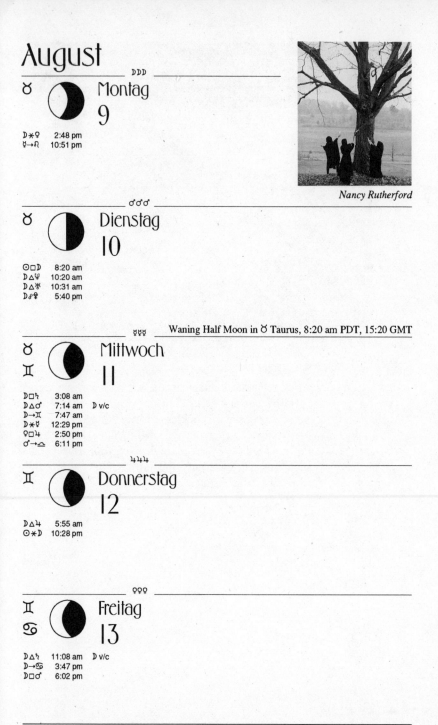

Nancy Rutherford

♉   ♂♂♂

◐ ## Dienstag
10

☉□☽   8:20 am
☽△♆   10:20 am
☽△♅   10:31 am
☽☍♀   5:40 pm

     ☿☿☿   Waning Half Moon in ♉ Taurus, 8:20 am PDT, 15:20 GMT

♉
♊ ◑ ## Mittwoch
11

☽□♄   3:08 am
☽△♂   7:14 am   ☽ v/c
☽→♊   7:47 am
☽⚹♅   12:29 pm
♀□♃   2:50 pm
♂→♎   6:11 pm

♊   ♃♃♃

◑ ## Donnerstag
12

☽△♃   5:55 am
☉⚹☽   10:28 pm

     ♀♀♀

♊
♋ ◗ ## Freitag
13

☽△♄   11:08 am   ☽ v/c
☽→♋   3:47 pm
☽□♂   6:02 pm

All aspects in Pacific Daylight Time; add 3 hours for EDT; add 7 hours for GMT

We spill salt in circles
Shout in minor keys.
We summon Diana Isis Hecate
We write wishes on rice paper—certain
We know what will make us happy.
We play at witchery
We want change in conformity to our whims.
We want the universe at our feet.

We breathe deep, suckling Earthblood.
Her Power fills our wombs, our breasts
Our hands, our circle.
We drink, overflow, shine like stars.
We concentrate, conjure magic symbols,
Howl like wolvewomen, chant Her Names.
We imprint wishes on Astral Planes, those
Liquid Worlds where futures rest
Ripe for manipulation, artistry.
We know a secret: Imagination is magic.
We burn and banish.
So mote it be.

We play at witchery—certain
We know what will make us happy.
We hope we know what we're doing.

Diana Rose Hartmann

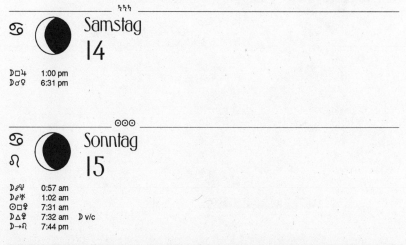

| ♋ | 🌓 | Samstag |
| | | 14 |

| ☽□♃ | 1:00 pm |
| ☽☌♀ | 6:31 pm |

| ♋ | 🌑 | Sonntag |
| ♌ | | 15 |

☽☍♆	0:57 am	
☽☍♅	1:02 am	
☉□♀	7:31 am	
☽△♀	7:32 am	☽ v/c
☽→♌	7:44 pm	

Blessing of the Bread

(To North)	From the Plowing to the Planting,
(To East)	To the Growing to the Ripening,
(To South)	To the Harvesting to the Grinding,
(To West)	To the Baking to the Breaking,
(To Center)	Blessed art Thou Creature of Earth,
	Body of the Goddess, by which
	SHE nurtures and sustains HER Children.
(To Each Other)	By HER are WE truly Blessed!

❂ *Lorain Karol 1986*

Rising of the Corn   © *Carolyn Hillyer 1991*

IX. EVERYDAY MAGIC MOON
we see you in all we do

Medicine Woman   © *Ruth Zachary*

août

*Huckleberry jam
all the tiredness
up in jars*

✿ *Jane Reichhold*

⟩⟩⟩

♌ lundi
16

☽✳︎♂ 0:12 am
☽♂♅ 2:37 pm
☽✳︎♃ 4:10 pm

♂♂♂

♌
♍ mardi
17

♅✳︎♃ 3:40 am
☽□♀ 9:05 am
☉♂♄ 12:29 pm
☽♂♄ 4:03 pm   ☽ v/c
☽→♍ 8:41 pm
♀♂♆ 9:53 pm
♀♂♅ 10:16 pm

☿☿☿

♍ mercredi
18

☽PrG 11:46 pm

♃♃♃

♍
♎ jeudi
19

☽△♆ 2:44 am
☽△♅ 2:45 am
☽✳︎♀ 5:13 am
☽✳︎♀ 9:05 am
☉♂♄ 4:01 pm   ☽ v/c
♄PrG 6:39 pm
☽→♎ 8:36 pm

♀♀♀

♎ vendredi
20

♅♂♆ 0:44 am
☽♂♂ 5:12 am
☽♂♃ 5:41 pm

All aspects in Pacific Daylight Time; add 3 hours for EDT; add 7 hours for GMT

VIRGO - Soil (AUGUST 22—SEPTEMBER 21)

1992 brought usually cautious Virgo out into center stage. A major cycle of growth began—you felt optimistic, you presented yourself with poise and self-confidence, and your world responded enthusiastically.

The cycle continues in '93 as Jupiter moves through your solar 2nd and 3rd houses. Your initiative-taking begins to bear fruit; you get a sense of the practical possibilities—they must reflect social needs. Resources are abundant but use self-restraint. You may begin advanced studies; your mind and understanding expand; plans and possibilities open up.

All planets are still below the horizon—Saturn makes a brief appearance above during May and June—but you are still preparing for an even bigger shift into the external world in the years ahead. You are still improving your style and techniques, preparing for a debut. '92-'93 finds you working in partnership and serving others, needing plenty of patience and adaptability.

Health crises are possible during such a time. Your body is a major tool; your ambitions for the future must respect your physical limits. Needs of body, mind and spirit must be balanced in your lifestyle. The seclusion and quiet reflection that accompany illness are catalysts that bring psychic and spiritual awakening or creative development. Illness also can be a necessary letting down of barriers to allow others in to help.

The dominating Uranus/Neptune configuration touches you in areas of creative expression, romance, children, fun. The inner child will demand time—play and pleasure must have their place in your life. There is joy to be felt in performing and shining, whatever the setting. Unusual loves/passions may appear and knock you right off your tidy purposeful perch, especially if you are being too serious or hardworking. Creative breakthroughs transform your techniques; children call out your most playful aspect.

© *Gretchen Lawlor 1992*

♎︎ ☽ samedi
♏︎   21

☽□♅	2:57 am		
☽□♆	2:58 am		
☽✶♅	5:43 am		
♀△♀	7:02 am	☉✶☽	7:52 pm ☽ v/c
☽□♀	9:49 am	☽→♏︎	9:28 pm
☽△♄	4:10 pm		

"My Desires Are Born in Her Caverns"
○ *Julie Hopp*

♏︎ ☽ dimanche
       22

| ♅□♀ | 10:08 am |
| ☉→♍︎ | 7:51 pm |

Sun in Virgo, 7:51 pm PDT
2:51 GMT (Aug. 23)

agosto

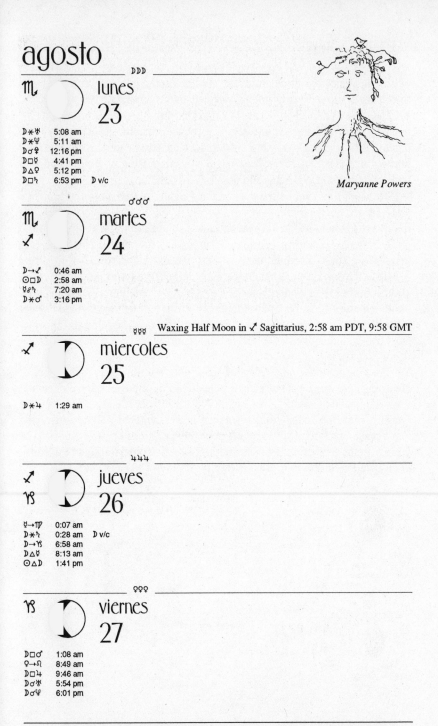

♌♌♌ _____

♏ 🌒 **lunes**
23

☽✶♅	5:08 am
☽✶♆	5:11 am
☽♂♀	12:16 pm
☽□♅	4:41 pm
☽△♀	5:12 pm
☽□♄	6:53 pm ☽ v/c

Maryanne Powers

_____ ♂♂♂ _____

♏
♐ 🌒 **martes**
24

☽→♐	0:46 am
☉□☽	2:58 am
♅☍♄	7:20 am
☽✶♂	3:16 pm

_____ ☿☿☿ Waxing Half Moon in ♐ Sagittarius, 2:58 am PDT, 9:58 GMT

♐ 🌓 **miercoles**
25

☽✶♃	1:29 am

_____ ♃♃♃ _____

♐
♑ 🌓 **jueves**
26

♅→♍	0:07 am
☽✶♄	0:28 am ☽ v/c
☽→♑	6:58 am
☽△♅	8:13 am
☉△☽	1:41 pm

_____ ♀♀♀ _____

♑ 🌓 **viernes**
27

☽□♂	1:08 am
♀→♌	8:49 am
☽□♃	9:46 am
☽♂♅	5:54 pm
☽♂♆	6:01 pm

_____

All aspects in Pacific Daylight Time; add 3 hours for EDT; add 7 hours for GMT

The Spirit of the Wind   © *Shoshana Rothaizer 1981*

A Mossy Mystery

I live amongst the mystery.
Tall Moss people
with greenly colored limbs
stand in circle around me
echoing their majik.

Gently, patiently,
these greenly creatures
pull me inside out
reversing my madness into majik.

❂ *Kelly Blue Sky 1992*

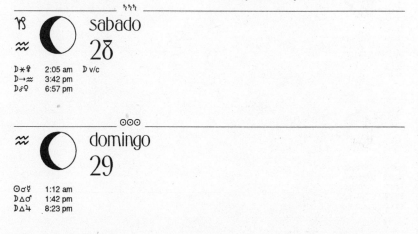

♑
≈   sabado
           28

☽⚹♀   2:05 am   ☽ v/c
☽→≈   3:42 pm
☽☍♀   6:57 pm

≈   domingo
           29

☉☌♅   1:12 am
☽△♂   1:42 pm
☽△♃   8:23 pm

August

≋  **Monday**
30

D□♀ 12:23 pm
D♂♄ 6:40 pm   D v/c

Robyn of Entropy

♂♂♂

≋
♓ **Tuesday**
31

D→♓ 2:19 pm
☉♂D 7:33 pm

"Blue Moon" (USA)
Full Moon in ♍ Virgo, 7:33 pm PDT
2:33 GMT

☿☿☿

♓ **Wednesday**
1

September

D♂♅ 1:51 am
D⚹♅ 3:11 pm
D⚹♆ 3:23 pm

♄♄♄

♓
♈ **Thursday**
2

D△♀ 0:12 am   D v/c
D→♈ 2:21 pm

♀♀♀

♈ **Friday**
3

D△♀ 7:03 am
DApG 10:02 am
D♂♂ 8:17 pm
D♂♃ 10:17 pm

All aspects in Pacific Daylight Time; add 3 hours for EDT; add 7 hours for GMT

© *Lava 1989*

ROSEMARY (Rosmarinus offincinalis)

In the small rituals of everyday life, one of our greatest needs is protection and the clearing of negative energies. In the European tradition rosemary is one of the oldest incenses used for this purpose. Rosemary wands, by themselves or dipped in saltwater, can be used to define sacred space, provide protection, or cleanse a house. It is also frequently burned to clear the air of harmful energy. Sacred to Isis and Mary.   © *Colette Gardiner 1992*

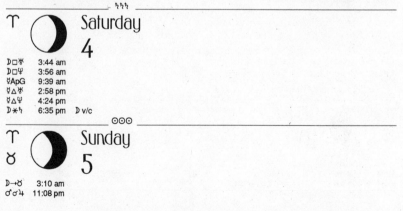

♈ Saturday
4

☽□♅	3:44 am
☽□Ψ	3:56 am
☿ApG	9:39 am
☿△♅	2:58 pm
☿△Ψ	4:24 pm
☽✶♄	6:35 pm ☽ v/c

♈
♉ Sunday
5

☽→♉	3:10 am
♂♂♃	11:08 pm

September

☽☽☽

© *Kit Cameron 1987*

♉ Montag 6

☽□♀	2:39 am
☉△☽	7:26 am
☽△♅	4:15 pm
☽△♆	4:29 pm

♂♂♂

♉ ♊ Dienstag 7

☽△☿	1:01 am	
☽☍♇	1:34 am	
☿✶♇	4:44 am	
☽□♄	6:34 am	☽ v/c
☽→♊	3:16 pm	

☿☿☿

♊ Mittwoch 8

☽✶♀	8:14 pm
☉□☽	11:27 pm
☽△♃	11:47 pm

♃♃♃

Waning Half Moon in ♉ Gemini, 11:27 pm PDT
6:27 GMT

♊ Donnerstag 9

☽△♂	2:33 am	
♂□♅	7:36 am	
♂□♆	12:16 pm	
☽△♄	4:08 pm	
☽□☿	8:24 pm	☽ v/c

♀♀♀

♊ ♋ Freitag 10

☽→♋	0:37 am
♀✶♃	3:59 pm
☉△♅	6:39 pm
☉△♆	9:56 pm

All aspects in Pacific Daylight Time; add 3 hours for EDT; add 7 hours for GMT

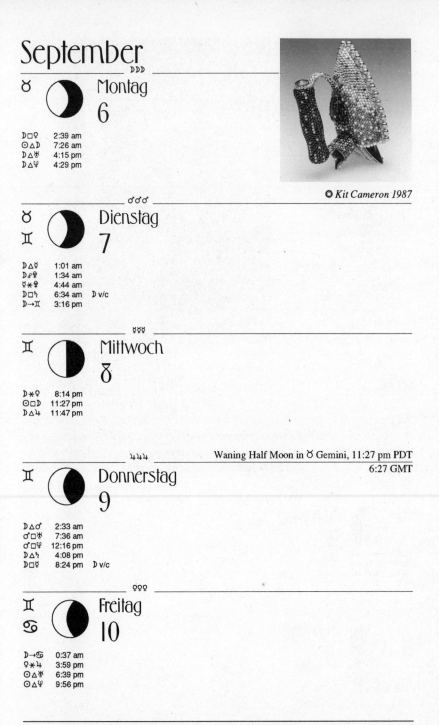

Felicia's Tea

Ritual means different things to different people. Some save their ceremonies for solstices and full moons, while others honor ritual in every-day ways. Felicia did both, but I best remember her as someone who would ritualize the smallest, most seemingly-ordinary events...

Felicia's Tea   © *Laurie York 1986*

♋ ☽ **Samstag**
11

♀→♎	4:19 am
☽□♃	7:44 am
☽☍♅	9:40 am
☽☍♆	9:54 am
☉⚹☽	10:50 am
☽□♂	12:15 pm
☽△♀	6:07 pm ☽ v/c

☉☉☉

♋ ☽ **Sonntag**
♌ **12**

☽→♌	5:52 am
☽⚹♅	9:20 am

septembre

DDD

"Origami"
she explained
folding up the bills

© Jane Reichhold

♌ lundi 13

☽✶♃ 11:23 am
☽☌♀ 4:24 pm
☽✶♂ 5:14 pm
☽□♇ 8:25 pm
☽☍♄ 11:32 pm ☽ v/c

♂♂♂

♌ ♍ mardi 14

☽→♍ 7:20 am
♀✶♂ 1:54 pm

☿☿☿

♍ mercredi 15

☽△♅ 12:20 pm
☽△♆ 12:34 pm
♀□♇ 6:16 pm
☉✶♇ 7:59 pm
☽✶♇ 8:10 pm
☉☌☽ 8:11 pm ☽ v/c

New Moon in ♍ Virgo, 8:11 pm PDT
3:11 GMT

♃♃♃

♍ ♎ jeudi 16

☽→♎ 6:44 am
☽PrG 7:45 am
♃□♅ 9:47 am
☽☌☿ 9:33 pm

♀♀♀

♎ vendredi 17

♃□♆ 2:31 am
♀☍♄ 3:42 am
☽□♅ 11:31 am
☽□♆ 11:45 am
☽☌♃ 11:53 am
☽☌♂ 8:39 pm
☽△♄ 10:05 pm
☽✶♀ 11:47 pm ☽ v/c

All aspects in Pacific Daylight Time; add 3 hours for EDT; add 7 hours for GMT

The Triple Goddess of Slime, Worms and Spuds

She is the principle Deity on our smallholding, as she reminds us of where and by whose work our food comes from.
All honour to the Goddess of Many Forms!
Blessed Be.

☉ *Nicola Beechsquirrel*

≗ ♋ ⚫   **samedi**
♏   **18**

☽→♏   6:15 am

♏ ⚫   **dimanche**
   19

♂△♄   2:27 am
☽✳♅   12:06 pm
☽✳♆   12:21 pm
☽♂♀   8:39 pm
☽□♄   11:03 pm

Voice of the Goddess

"Close your eyes," she said to me, "and breathe." At last her voice reached through the roar of instructions from voices I'd absorbed in all the years of being told what to do. She reminded me that this voice of truth in us "...is a voice of love. It is a voice that says you are all right, a voice that speaks gently and never tells you to hurt any being, any thing. It will never lead you into harm. There may be times when your thoughts will mimic this voice, but keep listening and you will know."

This inner voice reminds me each time to breathe and love. It works -- though I don't know how. Under her guidance, my breath itself becomes the path to love. I've come to where I can hear her for instant help as I go through my days, for by now I know she is always there. Just stop. And ask. And breathe. And listen.

✪ *Sunlight*

'She Is' Invocation

She is,	Earth; Powerful, strong, deep woman, arms holding us like her children.
She is,	Air; Fresh, light, soft, gentle woman caressing us like morning.
She is,	Fire; Hot, passionate, purifying woman, licking our center like a lover.
She is,	Water; Fierce, tranquil, ever changing woman, seeping into our souls like rain.
She is,	Spirit; Divine and daring, ever new woman born each second in our Souls.
She is,	here.

© *Kris Russell 1991*

X. MEDITATION MOON
let us hear you in the silence

© Deborah Koff-Chapin

septiembre)))

♏ | ☽ | **lunes**
♐ | | **20**

☉⚹☽ 3:37 am
☽□♀ 5:40 am   ☽ v/c
☽→♐ 7:54 am

♂♂♂

♐ | ☽ | **martes**
| | **21**

♀→♍ 7:23 am
☽⚹♅ 12:53 pm
☽⚹♃ 5:44 pm

☿☿☿

♐ | ☽ | **miercoles**
♑ | | **22**

☽⚹♄ 3:13 am
☽⚹♂ 7:24 am
☉□☽ 12:33 pm   ☽ v/c
☽→♑ 12:54 pm
♅□♆ 1:59 pm
☽△♀ 3:56 pm
♅□♆ 4:26 pm
☉→♎ 5:23 pm

Waxing Half Moon in ♐ Sagittarius, 12:33 pm PDT
19:33 GMT

Solstice

Sun in Libra 5:23 am PST
0:23 GMT

♃♃♃

♑ | ☽ | **jueves**
| | **23**

♅☌♃ 2:47 pm
☽☌♅ 10:50 pm
☽☌♆ 11:07 pm

♀♀♀

♑ | ☽ | **viernes**
≈ | | **24**

☽□♃ 1:57 am
☽□♅ 3:13 am
☽⚹♀ 8:49 am
☽□♂ 6:42 pm   ☽ v/c
☽→≈ 9:19 pm

All aspects in Pacific Daylight Time; add 3 hours for EDT; add 7 hours for GMT

LIBRA - Breath

(SEPTEMBER 22—OCTOBER 22)

1993-a good year for Libra. Jupiter transits Libra from Oct. '92- Nov. '93, emphasizing your artistic talents and relating skills. This is the beginning of a major cycle of growth; right now you feel adventurous. You are optimistic about your capabilities and confident that you will do well. This inspires those around you, and they will do all they can to help you. Collaborative efforts are blessed.

Uranus/Neptune reach their exact conjunction in Capricorn during 1993 and each sign is already manifesting a particular facet of this breakdown/breakthrough experience. Librans feel it in a deep insecurity. Ties with the past are broken, and you feel you have lost your roots. You are being freed from old patterns and habits that have held you from being committed to your present circumstances. Moments of utter devastation, of feeling awash at sea intermingle with moments of insight, feelings of mystical belonging. You may suddenly move home, or you may have already in the past couple of years. However, your security lies in association with people who share your principles and ideals, rather than in biological units or specific locations. You may be providing the security of home for a group or a sanctuary for friends.

Saturn in Aquarius ('92-'93) emphasizes the strength and solidity of the smaller group—the neighborhood, the community, the tribe, in times of worldwide disorder. Even within these smaller units there will be turbulence, but it will feel manageable. You will struggle with how to balance your individual needs with the group direction, and herein lies your greatest lesson. You have a creative role—it may be your responsibility to remind others to play, to be adventurous, to honor the children. In providing this for others, you free up your own inner playfulness. Take courage Libra, step out—others will follow. © *Gretchen Lawlor 1992*

♒ ◑ sabado
25

☉△☽   1:46 am

♒ ◐ domingo
26

☽△♃   1:10 pm
☿△♄   7:15 pm
♂→♏   7:16 pm
☽□♀   7:25 pm
☽♂♄   9:08 pm
☽△♅   9:24 pm   ☽ v/c

"Beaver Island" ☾ *Rosa*

September ♌♌♌

♒
♓ 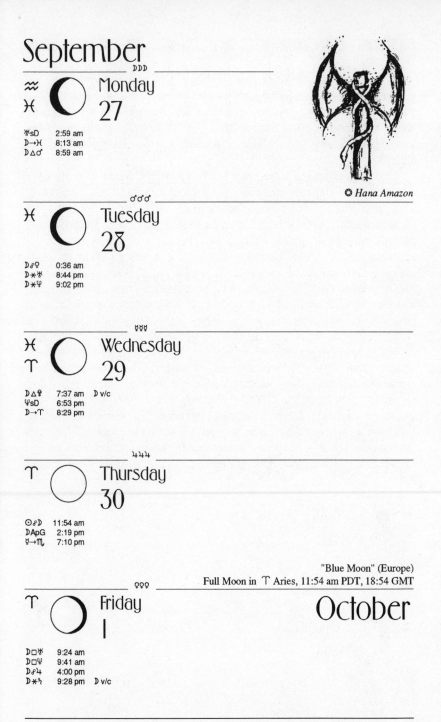 ## Monday
27

♅sD   2:59 am
☽→♓   8:13 am
☽△♂   8:59 am

© *Hana Amazon*

♂♂♂

♓ ## Tuesday
28

☽☍♀   0:36 am
☽✶♅   8:44 pm
☽✶♆   9:02 pm

☿☿☿

♓
♈ ## Wednesday
29

☽△♇   7:37 am   ☽ v/c
♆sD   6:53 pm
☽→♈   8:29 pm

♃♃♃

♈ ## Thursday
30

☉☍☽   11:54 am
☽ApG   2:19 pm
☿→♏   7:10 pm

"Blue Moon" (Europe)
Full Moon in ♈ Aries, 11:54 am PDT, 18:54 GMT

♀♀♀

♈ ## Friday
1

October

☽□♅   9:24 am
☽□♆   9:41 am
☽☍♃   4:00 pm
☽✶♄   9:28 pm   ☽ v/c

All aspects in Pacific Daylight Time; add 3 hours for EDT; add 7 hours for GMT

A Bee Whispers What It Knows   © *Sudie Rakusin 1984*

A Gentler Echo

What is my path?   Who will guide me?
My path.   Me.
What must I do?   How will I know?
Do.   Know.   ❂ *Erin A. Deluna*

♈   ☽   ♄♄♄ Saturday
♉   2

D→♉   9:14 am
D☍♅   2:04 pm
D☍♂   5:20 pm

─────── ☉☉☉ ───────

♉   ☽   Sunday
                     3

D△♀   3:42 pm
D△♅   10:00 pm
D△♆   10:16 pm

Oktober

ᎠᎠᎠ

♉
Ⅱ
Montag
4

☽☌♀ 9:05 am
☽□♄ 9:42 am ☽ v/c
☽→Ⅱ 9:27 pm

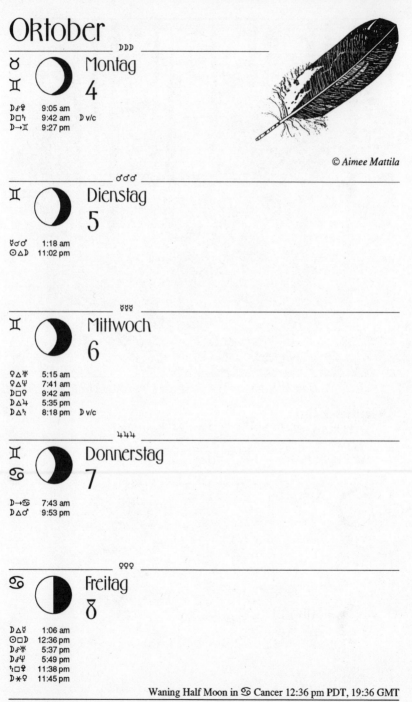

© *Aimee Mattila*

♂♂♂

Ⅱ
Dienstag
5

♉♂♂ 1:18 am
☉△☽ 11:02 pm

☿☿☿

Ⅱ
Mittwoch
6

♀△♅ 5:15 am
♀△♆ 7:41 am
☽□♀ 9:42 am
☽△♃ 5:35 pm
☽△♄ 8:18 pm ☽ v/c

♃♃♃

Ⅱ
♋
Donnerstag
7

☽→♋ 7:43 am
☽△♂ 9:53 pm

♀♀♀

♋
Freitag
8

☽△♅ 1:06 am
☉□☽ 12:36 pm
☽☍♅ 5:37 pm
☽☍♆ 5:49 pm
♄□♀ 11:38 pm
☽⚹♀ 11:45 pm

Waning Half Moon in ♋ Cancer 12:36 pm PDT, 19:36 GMT

All aspects in Pacific Daylight Time; add 3 hours for EDT; add 7 hours for GMT

© Melissa Harris 1992

LINDEN
(Tilia spp.)

The blossoms of this tree can be used as a tea or tincture to bring peace and calm, to help create a sense of stillness where we can listen for the balance. In England, elaborate pruning techniques were used to create a living trellis. They were seen as quiet resting areas secluded from the cares of everyday life and the demands of people. Linden is also used as a strong tea on a daily basis to help clear cholesterol from the blood. Linden is associated with Venus or Lada.

♋︎
♌︎

Samstag
9

☽□♃	2:17 am	
☽△♀	3:48 pm	☽ v/c
☽→♌︎	2:34 pm	

♌︎

Sonntag
10

☽□♂	6:33 am	
☽□♅	11:35 am	
♀⚹♀	8:48 pm	
☉⚹☽	9:24 pm	

Octobre

☽☽☽

♌ ♍

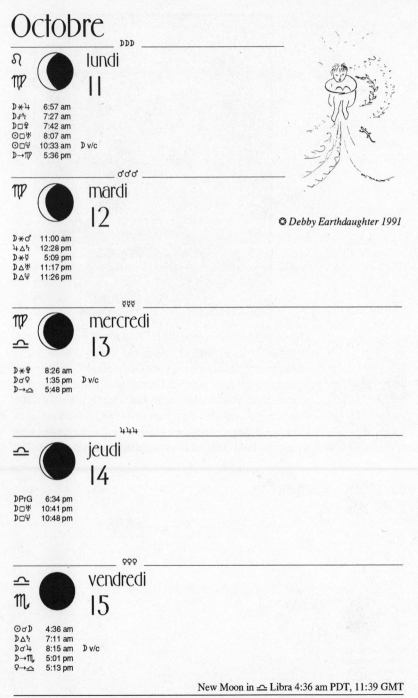

lundi 11

☽✶♃ 6:57 am
☽☍♄ 7:27 am
☽□♇ 7:42 am
☉□♅ 8:07 am
☉□♆ 10:33 am ☽ v/c
☽→♍ 5:36 pm

© Debby Earthdaughter 1991

♂♂♂

♍

mardi 12

☽✶♂ 11:00 am
♃△♄ 12:28 pm
☽✶☿ 5:09 pm
☽△♅ 11:17 pm
☽△♆ 11:26 pm

☿☿☿

♍ ♎

mercredi 13

☽✶♇ 8:26 am
☽☌♀ 1:35 pm ☽ v/c
☽→♎ 5:48 pm

♃♃♃

♎

jeudi 14

☽PrG 6:34 pm
☽□♅ 10:41 pm
☽□♆ 10:48 pm

♀♀♀

♎ ♏

vendredi 15

☉☌☽ 4:36 am
☽△♄ 7:11 am
☽☌♃ 8:15 am ☽ v/c
☽→♏ 5:01 pm
♀→♎ 5:13 pm

New Moon in ♎ Libra 4:36 am PDT, 11:39 GMT

All aspects in Pacific Daylight Time; add 3 hours for EDT; add 7 hours for GMT

"Kakaken" also called by name of "Dance of Hiten," is an old Chinese way of meditation through movement. In the deep breathing, together with a silent movement, the energy of the universe is sucked into the body, and it is aimed to activate the inner energy in order to regulate the nerves and internal organs and the inner secretions.

photo and text by Cathy Cade ©1990

♏ ⏾ ♌♌♌ **samedi**
16

♃ApG	1:12 pm
☽♂♂	2:36 pm
☉△♄	7:28 pm
☿✶♅	8:46 pm
☽✶♅	10:25 pm
☽♂☿	10:31 pm
☽✶Ψ	10:31 pm

☿✶Ψ 10:39 pm

☉☉☉

♏ ⏾ **dimanche**
♐ **17**

☽□♄	7:06 am
☽♂♀	7:54 am
☽→♐	5:24 pm
☽✶♀	9:55 pm

☽ v/c

Golden Light

Medicine animals call,
Invite me to their lair.
Spirit ones of the deer and wolf clan.
Dancers on the dreamwheel.

I ride on the cobalt lizard's back
        to the underworld,
Along the rooted one's channels.
Shapeshifting into great mother serpent,
Gliding effortlessly down passageways
        toward a cave.

Magnificent journey.
Levels and levels revealed,
Through valleys and meadows of heartland.
Mystery is momentarily knowable, sacred.

Anubis introduces me to my soul,
Guards the old ways and escorts them,
Walks slowly through the gate of
        sovereign judges,
Carries the rotting self like an old skin
        discarded.

It is the time of separating paths.
Outmoded relationships crumble earthward.
In retreat, the veils are gently peeled away.
A child is born, her new life revealed.

Hathor leads the merriment.
White wolf, doe, and fawn initiate the dance.
Great Goddess of love and joy whose body is
        the sun and moon,
Completes the underworld journey and
        sends me home.

✪ *Gentle Doe*

XI. SHAPE-SHIFTING MOON
journey with us to our depths,
that we may find wholeness

Creatress   © *Vicki Ledray Grabicki 1988*

octubre

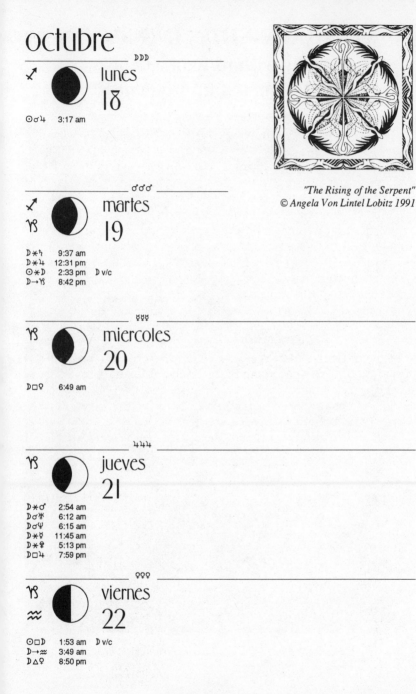

♐ ☽☽☽ _____
lunes
18

⊙♂♃   3:17 am

♐
♑ ♂♂♂ _____
martes
19

☽⚹♄   9:37 am
☽⚹♃   12:31 pm
⊙⚹☽   2:33 pm   ☽ v/c
☽→♑   8:42 pm

♑ ☿☿☿ _____
miercoles
20

☽□♀   6:49 am

♑ ♃♃♃ _____
jueves
21

☽⚹♂   2:54 am
☽♂♅   6:12 am
☽♂♆   6:15 am
☽⚹♇   11:45 am
☽⚹♀   5:13 pm
☽□♃   7:59 pm

♑
♒ ♀♀♀ _____
viernes
22

⊙□☽   1:53 am   ☽ v/c
☽→♒   3:49 am
☽△♀   8:50 pm

"The Rising of the Serpent"
© Angela Von Lintel Lobitz 1991

Waxing Half Moon in ♑ Capricorn, 11:53 am PDT, 8:53 GMT

All aspects in Pacific Daylight Time; add 3 hours for EDT; add 7 hours for GMT

SCORPIO - *Geyser*　　　　(OCTOBER 23—NOVEMBER 20)

Scorpio continues the slow shedding of old skins, but now the bottom layer is in sight, glistening with promise just below the surface. As Pluto reaches the latter degrees of your sign and Jupiter enters Scorpio (late '93), your painful preoccupation with self-transformation lessens. Life lightens up.

As movement towards this breakthrough occurs, fear and resistance to dealing with your less desirable sides dissolves. Religion, metaphysics, meditation—all provide you with support and understanding of yourself. Your inner work of the past years has given you a strong compassion and ability to empathize with the struggles of others. A guide/teacher appears for a while in '92-'93 to help you in your coming out—don't look for the standard guru garb.

Saturn is in the latter part of your solar 4th house, completing a phase of hard work which establishes the basics of security and survival. Many Scorpions are building or transforming home, establishing a stable, secure environment. Immense uncertainties in the outer world prompt you to establish an inner, personal center of tranquility.

Your greatest upsets and most exciting opportunities for change will come from your neighborhood, community, immediate environment. Your mind is being bombarded with new thoughts; you are being continually forced to let go of obsolete attitudes/expectations. If you have been quite a rational thinker, you will find the sudden flashes of inspiration and irrationality of Uranus/Neptune disturbing. Psychic abilities continue to manifest. You have an ability to grab potent images of the times and express them through words—others will listen. Watch for chances to collaborate, it is not a time to work in solitude. Be flexible, give thanks for something every day, ask for help from friends and be open to the divine.

© *Gretchen Lawlor 1992*

♒ | sábado | Sun in Scorpio 2:38 am PST, 9:38 GMT
23

☉→♏	2:38 am
☽□♂	3:29 pm
♂⚹♅	5:57 pm
♂⚹♆	6:13 pm
☽□♀	11:06 pm

♒ | domingo
♓ | **24**

☽♂♄	1:42 am
☽□♀	3:20 am
☽△♃	7:08 am
♅♂♆	1:18 pm　☽ v/c
☽→♓	2:18 pm
☉△☽	5:31 pm

"Tiger Lily" © *Genece Klein 1990*

October

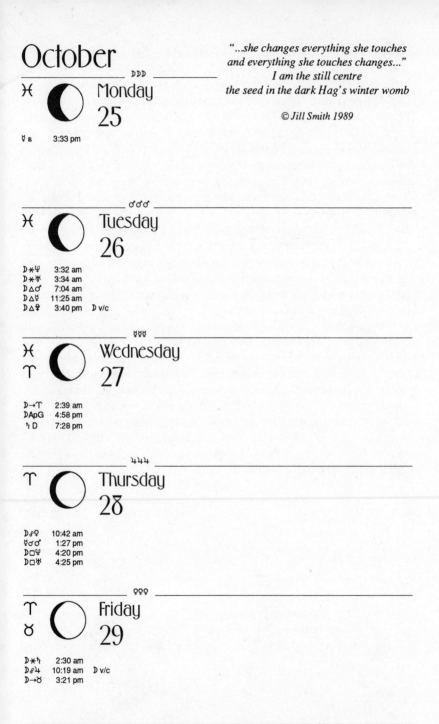

"...she changes everything she touches
and everything she touches changes..."
I am the still centre
the seed in the dark Hag's winter womb

☽☽☽

♓ Monday 25

☿ R 3:33 pm

♂♂♂

♓ Tuesday 26

☽✶♆ 3:32 am
☽✶♅ 3:34 am
☽△♂ 7:04 am
☽△☿ 11:25 am
☽△♇ 3:40 pm ☽ v/c

☿☿☿

♓ ♈ Wednesday 27

☽→♈ 2:39 am
☽ApG 4:58 pm
♄ D 7:28 pm

♃♃♃

♈ Thursday 28

☽☍♀ 10:42 am
☿☌♂ 1:27 pm
☽□♆ 4:20 pm
☽□♅ 4:25 pm

♀♀♀

♈ ♉ Friday 29

☽✶♄ 2:30 am
☽☍♃ 10:19 am ☽ v/c
☽→♉ 3:21 pm

Endarkening *

Conjuring up the shadows
Watching them spiral in and out of our lives
Putting a new dark on things

Invoking inward energy
Going inside the dark
Inviting insight, intuition
Making invisible that which needs protection
Endarkening...

Valuing the cave, the womb, the night
Gestating, germanating, releasing, resting
Being that which lives instead of
That which watches
Endarkening

Experiencing ecstasy
Eroticism in the dark
Experiencing pure sensation
Sensing with the heart, the hands, the belly. . .

Feeling depth in the dark
Following dark wisdom which does not
        need to know
Flowing with the dark
Claiming the freedom to move as we chose
        in the dark
Finding that it nurtures
        as it endarkens

Opening to the dark
Reveling in mystery that
Reveals dark truth
Revering our female truth
Letting no man talk us out of it
Returning joyfully to the dark inside
Endarkening.

                                    ✪ *Antiga*

* *Thanks to Amber K for the word and many of the images in
this poem.*

Hallowmas

Time of Hag   Time of Crone
Time of Blood Time of Bone

Hecate offers cold embrace
Spectre, wraith and banshee pace

Wait for Hallow's eve to fly
Wait 'til deepest dark to scry

This night the veil is very thin
Life goes out and death comes in

Open wide to all the fear
Trust that from the darkness here

Life and light will rise again
Death goes out and life comes in

**Mask for
Samhain**

✪ *Sheila Broun*

Crone Tree   © *Carolyn Hillyer*

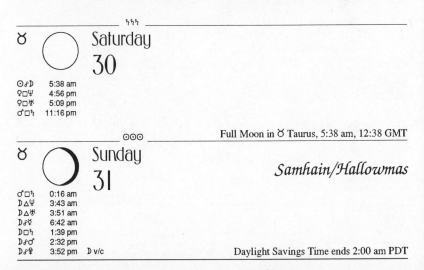

ⰔⰔⰔ

♉   ◯   **Saturday**
              30

☉☍☽   5:38 am
♀□♆   4:56 pm
♀□♅   5:09 pm
♂□♄   11:16 pm

◉◉◉

Full Moon in ♉ Taurus, 5:38 am, 12:38 GMT

♉   ◯   **Sunday**
              31

♂□♄   0:16 am
☽△♆   3:43 am
☽△♅   3:51 am
☽☍♉   6:42 am
☽□♄   1:39 pm
☽☍♂   2:32 pm
☽☍♀   3:52 pm   ☽ v/c

Samhain/Hallowmas

Daylight Savings Time ends 2:00 am PDT

November

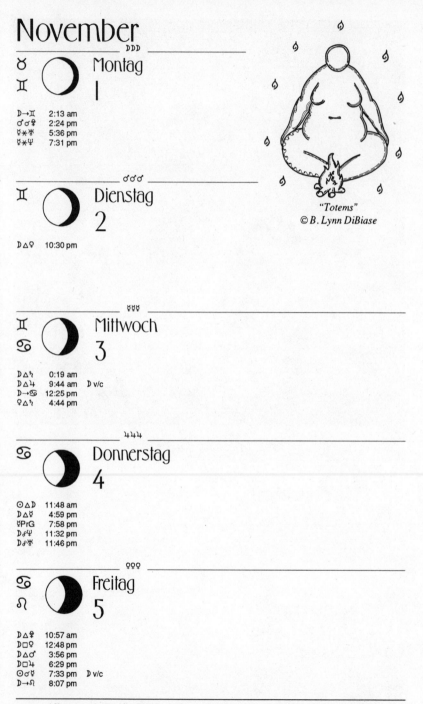

"Totems"
© B. Lynn DiBiase

♉
♊   Montag
1

☽→♊   2:13 am
♂☌♀   2:24 pm
☿⚹♅   5:36 pm
☿⚹♆   7:31 pm

♊   Dienstag
2

☽△♀   10:30 pm

♊
♋   Mittwoch
3

☽△♄   0:19 am
☽△♃   9:44 am   ☽ v/c
☽→♋   12:25 pm
♀△♄   4:44 pm

♋   Donnerstag
4

☉△☽   11:48 am
☽△☿   4:59 pm
☿PrG   7:58 pm
☽☍♆   11:32 pm
☽☍♅   11:46 pm

♋
♌   Freitag
5

☽△♀   10:57 am
☽□♀   12:48 pm
☽△♂   3:56 pm
☽□♃   6:29 pm
☉☌☿   7:33 pm   ☽ v/c
☽→♌   8:07 pm

All aspects in Pacific Standard Time; add 3 hours for EST; add 8 hours for GMT

© *Sudie Rakusin 1987*

BELLADONA (Atropa Belladona)
As we become wise women we can claim our darkness and use it to journey between the worlds. Unfortunately, the knowledge to use herbs accurately for astral projection has been mostly destroyed in many cultures and is being actively eradicated in others. Belladona (nightshade) is a deadly poison that was once used to aid in visits to other realms, not just by witches but in Roman times as well. Today the vines can be used to create a circle to do work on deep issues. It provides strong banishing energy while we go inside to release serious hurts and abuses. **No part of the plant should be ingested!** Sacred to Hecate. © *Colette Gardiner 1992*

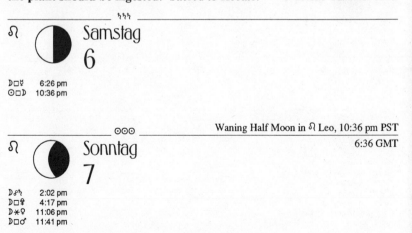

♌ ◑ Samstag
6

ꙍ♏♄

☽□☿ 6:26 pm
☉□☽ 10:36 pm

♌ ◑ Sonntag
7

☉☉☉

Waning Half Moon in ♌ Leo, 10:36 pm PST
6:36 GMT

☽☌♄ 2:02 pm
☽□♀ 4:17 pm
☽⚹♀ 11:06 pm
☽□♂ 11:41 pm

novembre))))

*Magic symbols
drawn with blood
this holy space*

✪ *Jane Reichhold*

♌
♍   ## lundi
8

☽✶♃	0:04 am	☽ v/c
☽→♍	0:48 am	
♀♂♃	11:57 am	
☽✶♅	5:53 pm	
♀→♏	6:07 pm	
♂→♐	9:30 pm	

—— ♂♂♂ ——

♍   ## mardi
9

☉✶☽	5:39 am
☽△♆	8:23 am
☽△♅	8:41 am
☽✶♀	6:45 pm ☽ v/c

—— ☿☿☿ ——

♍
♎   ## mercredi
10

☽→♎	2:43 am
☽✶♂	4:12 am
☉✶♆	9:57 pm

—— ♃♃♃ ——

♎   ## jeudi
11

☉✶♅	2:57 am
☽□♆	9:11 am
☽□♅	9:31 am
☽△♄	5:07 pm ☽ v/c

—— ♀♀♀ ——

♎
♏   ## vendredi
12

☽→♏	3:00 am
☽♂♃	3:44 am
☽PrG	4:01 am
☽♂♀	10:22 am
☽♂♅	2:16 pm

All aspects in Pacific Standard Time; add 3 hours for EST; add 8 hours for GMT

Cerce © *V. S. Sekhmet 1989*

Hecate's Feast

At the cave's mouth
Hecate in her black hood
opens the seam between the
    worlds.
Under the dark moon
we split a pomegranate
and count the seeds
on our fingers.

excerpt ✪ *Marcia Cohee*

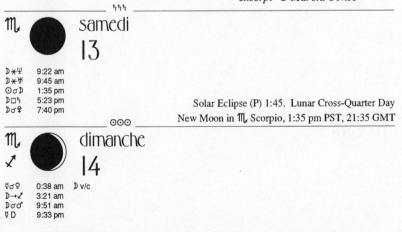

♏ ⟡ **samedi**
        13

☽⚹♆ 9:22 am
☽⚹♅ 9:45 am
☉☌☽ 1:35 pm
☽□♄ 5:23 pm
☽☌♀ 7:40 pm

Solar Eclipse (P) 1:45. Lunar Cross-Quarter Day
New Moon in ♏ Scorpio, 1:35 pm PST, 21:35 GMT

♏ ⟡ **dimanche**
♐   **14**

♅☌♀ 0:38 am ☽ v/c
☽→♐ 3:21 am
☽☌♂ 9:51 am
☿D 9:33 pm

Cast the Bones

Who will cast the bones
fling sticks
shuffle cards
read stones to tell me
Who will cast the bones?

Who will shuffle cards
read stones
draw runes
look in crystal balls
 to tell me
Who will shuffle cards?

Who will draw runes
look in crystal balls
see with third eye
or scry to tell me
Who will draw runes?

Who will see with third eye
or scry
or call spirits to tell me
Who will see with third eye?

Who will scry
or call spirits to tell me
Who will scry?

Who will call spirits
 to tell me
Who will call spirits?

Who will call to tell me?
Who will call?

excerpt © Ila Suzanne 1988

✪ *Kiwani*

XII. ORACLE MOON
open the crack between the worlds
that we may know our truth

noviembre
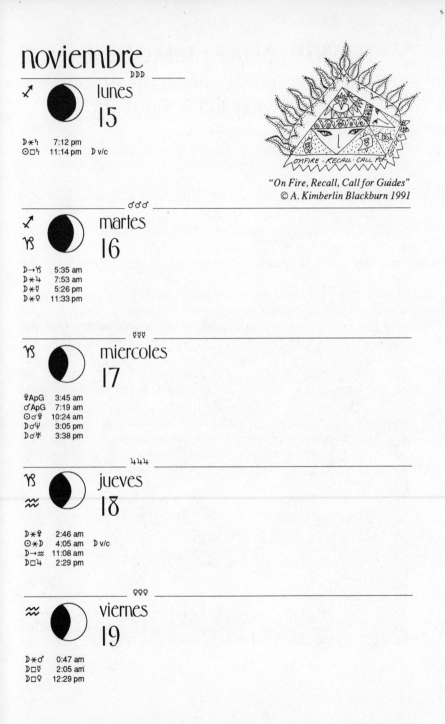

♐ 🌒 **lunes**
15

☽✶♄ 7:12 pm
☉□♄ 11:14 pm   ☽ v/c

♂♂♂

♐ 🌓 **martes**
♑   **16**

☽→♑ 5:35 am
☽✶♃ 7:53 am
☽✶♀ 5:26 pm
☽✶♀ 11:33 pm

☿☿☿

♑ 🌓 **miercoles**
          17

♀ApG 3:45 am
♂ApG 7:19 am
☉♂♀ 10:24 am
☽♂♆ 3:05 pm
☽♂♅ 3:38 pm

♃♃♃

♑ 🌓 **jueves**
♒   **18**

☽✶♀ 2:46 am
☉✶☽ 4:05 am   ☽ v/c
☽→♒ 11:08 am
☽□♃ 2:29 pm

♀♀♀

♒ 🌓 **viernes**
          19

☽✶♂ 0:47 am
☽□♅ 2:05 am
☽□♀ 12:29 pm

"On Fire, Recall, Call for Guides"
© A. Kimberlin Blackburn 1991

All aspects in Pacific Standard Time; add 3 hours for EST; add 8 hours for GMT

SAGITTARIUS - *Wildfire* (November 21—December 20)

The soaring spirit of Sagittarius does well in radical times. You are—we all are—experiencing a breakdown/breakthrough of consciousness during '92-'93: a gateway. Old forms dissolve, new ones appear overnight in their place, along with bouts of confusion and disorientation.

Sagittarius fortunes go through ups and downs with the Neptune/Uranus conjunction in your house of material resources and values. You need to keep your material conditions in order; you are prone to deceptions. You feel unsure about your true worth and inner values. Sudden opportunities reveal your gifts: artistic and creative imagination and ability to heal.

Gain comes through friends and group efforts—don't go it alone at present; the power is in collective efforts. It's awkward, even threatening at times, as you struggle to maintain your own individuality while exploring your position within the group.

It is likely you will occasionally retreat from all this change into rigidity and obstinacy. However, adaptation (mutation?) is the only way to survive the times. You have at your disposal a wonderful originality, inventiveness and moments of crystal clear insights. You need to find words/images for this creativity—people need your perspective.

Pluto hovering in the last degrees of Scorpio gives you glimpses of what you are capable of becoming. It can be frightening. You glimpse mighty personal changes ahead. Your hidden side acts up when you least expect it, and unresolved emotional problems come up to be dealt with now .The purpose of limitations/outer defeats experienced at this time is to help you hone your skills and find the very best outlets for expression. The asteroid Pallas in Aquarius, Feb.-April and Sept.-Dec., emphasizes creativity with words.

© *Gretchen Lawlor 1992*

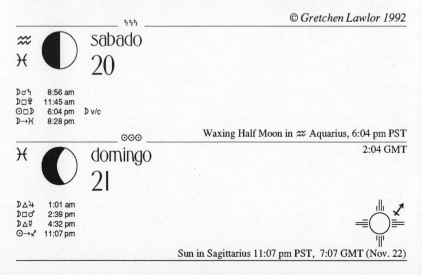

♒
♓   sabado
         20

D♂♄   8:56 am
D□♀   11:45 am
⊙□D   6:04 pm   D v/c
D→♓   8:28 pm

Waxing Half Moon in ♒ Aquarius, 6:04 pm PST
2:04 GMT

♓   domingo
         21

D△♃   1:01 am
D□♂   2:39 pm
D△♅   4:32 pm
⊙→♐   11:07 pm

Sun in Sagittarius 11:07 pm PST, 7:07 GMT (Nov. 22)

November ⟩⟩⟩

♓ 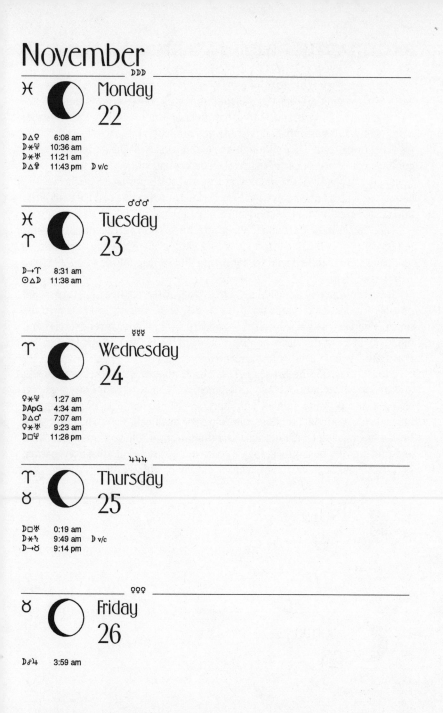 Monday
22

☽△♀   6:08 am
☽✶Ψ   10:36 am
☽✶♅   11:21 am
☽△♇   11:43 pm   ☽ v/c

♂♂♂

♓
♈   Tuesday
23

☽→♈   8:31 am
☉△☽   11:38 am

☿☿☿

♈   Wednesday
24

♀✶Ψ   1:27 am
☽ApG 4:34 am
☽△♂   7:07 am
♀✶♅   9:23 am
☽□Ψ   11:28 pm

♄♄♄

♈
♉   Thursday
25

☽□♅   0:19 am
☽✶♄   9:49 am   ☽ v/c
☽→♉   9:14 pm

♀♀♀

♉   Friday
26

☽☍♃   3:59 am

All aspects in Pacific Standard Time; add 3 hours for EST; add 8 hours for GMT

The Self and Other Dreams   © *Emerald Goldman*

ᕁᕁᕁ

♉ ◐ **Saturday**
27

☽☌♅ 6:19 am
☽△♆ 11:45 am
☽△♅ 12:40 pm
☽☌♀ 9:00 pm
☽□♄ 9:56 pm

⊙⊙⊙

♉ ◯ **Sunday**
♊   **28**

☽☌♀ 0:40 am
♀□♄ 6:24 am   ☽ v/c
☽→♊ 8:48 am
⊙☌☽ 10:31 pm

Lunar Eclipse (T), 10:26 pm PST, 6:26 GMT (Nov. 29)
Full Moon in ♊ Gemini, 10:31 pm PST, 6:31 GMT (Nov. 29)

November ⅅⅅⅅ

(Mask) © Lillian Pitt

♊ ◐ **Montag**
29

☿⚹♆ 8:27 am
♀☌♀ 9:42 am
☽☍♂ 1:52 pm
☿⚹♅ 5:16 pm

♂♂♂

♊
♋ ◐ **Dienstag**
30

☽△♄ 8:05 am   ☽ v/c
☽→♋ 6:18 pm

☿☿☿

♋ ◐ **Mittwoch**
I

Dezember

☽△♃ 2:25 am

♃♃♃

♋ ◐ **Donnerstag**
2

☽☍♆ 6:21 am
☽☍♅ 7:20 am
☽△☿ 2:35 pm
♀→♐ 3:54 pm
☽△♀ 6:23 pm   ☽ v/c

♀♀♀

♋
♌ ◐ **Freitag**
3

☽→♌ 1:33 am
☽△♀ 2:34 am
☿□♄ 3:50 am
☽□♃ 10:11 am
☉△☽ 11:20 pm

All aspects in Pacific Standard Time; add 3 hours for EST; add 8 hours for GMT

© *Melissa Harris 1992*

BAY
(Laurus
nobilis)

Bay's powers are protection, psychic awareness, purification, healing and strength. Priestesses at Delphi chewed fresh bay leaves to induce visions. The dried herb was burned and the smoke inhaled. A few leaves brewed into a tea also increases psychic awareness and helps to impart wisdom. Bay leaves can also be added to dream pillows for prophetic dreaming. It is associated with the Goddess Ceres and to a lesser degree with Athena.   © *Colette Gardiner 1992*

♌ ☽ Samstag
4

☿☌♀	1:46 am
☽△♂	10:47 am
☽☍♄	9:45 pm
☽□♀	11:58 pm

♌ ☽ Sonntag
♍   5

☽□♅	2:34 am	☽ v/c
☽→♍	6:43 am	
☽□♀	1:01 pm	
☽✳4	3:47 pm	

decembre ⅅⅅⅅ

♍ **lundi**

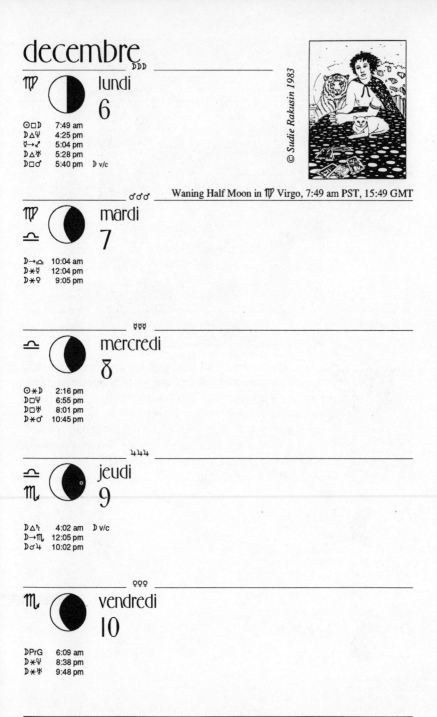

6

☉□ⅅ 7:49 am
ⅅ△♆ 4:25 pm
♅→♐ 5:04 pm
ⅅ△♅ 5:28 pm
ⅅ□♂ 5:40 pm ⅅ v/c

© Sudie Rakusin 1983

—————————— ♂♂♂ ——————————
Waning Half Moon in ♍ Virgo, 7:49 am PST, 15:49 GMT

♍
♎ **mardi**

7

ⅅ→♎ 10:04 am
ⅅ✳♅ 12:04 pm
ⅅ✳♀ 9:05 pm

—————————— ☿☿☿ ——————————

♎ **mercredi**

8

☉✳ⅅ 2:16 pm
ⅅ□♆ 6:55 pm
ⅅ□♅ 8:01 pm
ⅅ✳♂ 10:45 pm

—————————— ♃♃♃ ——————————

♎
♏ **jeudi**

9

ⅅ△♄ 4:02 am ⅅ v/c
ⅅ→♏ 12:05 pm
ⅅ♂♃ 10:02 pm

—————————— ♀♀♀ ——————————

♏ **vendredi**

10

ⅅPrG 6:09 am
ⅅ✳♆ 8:38 pm
ⅅ✳♅ 9:48 pm

—————————————————————————————
All aspects in Pacific Standard Time; add 3 hours for EST; add 8 hours for GMT

The Kwan Yin *

Coins
falling on cherished cloth
lines formed
six times
a hexagram revealed

Coins
brought from my root place
each side holds a symbol
the Irish harp
the Celtic knot
connects me to my ancestors

Coins
falling on cherished cloth
form into ancient language
hieroglyphics
I practice translations
these lines
translate into practice...

...In times of struggle
when my path is unclear
in times of pain
when all is bleak
in times of joy
when reflection is sought

© Sudie Rakusin 1986

Coins
falling on cherished cloth
guide me
to my center.

* dedicated to Diane Stein, author of
The Kuan Yin Book of Changes

excerpt, © Ni Aodagain 1992

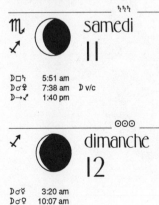

♏︎ ♐︎ samedi
11

☽□♄ 5:51 am
☽☌♀ 7:38 am ☽ v/c
☽→♐︎ 1:40 pm

♐︎ dimanche
12

☽☌♅ 3:20 am
☽☌♀ 10:07 am

The crickets hiccup after dark as I look for the fairy baby. The fairies hold my hand and we whisper secrets. They show me their lights and their doors between the cracks in the air. I listen to the sound of the dog barking, and the people whispering in the night. The sound stops when I enter the fairy door. I will live there forever and wear flowers and a crown of pure gold. The light shines from under the fairy door. Little bells tingle in the night, calling me. I turn once more to see the fairy baby. The door opens and I am gone.

✪ V.S. Sekhmet

© *Judith Burros*

XIII. ELEMENTAL MOON
introduce us to your many spirit realms

Shereon

diciembre ♌♌♌

♐
♑

lunes
13

☉☌☽   1:27 am
☽☌♂   7:58 am
☽✶♄   8:19 am
♂✶♄   3:19 pm   ☽ v/c
☽→♑   4:06 pm

___

♂♂♂   New Moon in ♐ Sagittarius, 1:27 am PST, 9:27 GMT

♑

martes
14

☽✶♃   3:50 am

___

☿☿☿

♑
♒

miercoles
15

☽☌♆   2:42 am
☽☌♅   4:05 am
☽✶♀   2:36 pm   ☽ v/c
☽→♒   8:52 pm

___

♃♃♃

♒

jueves
16

☽□♃   10:02 am

___

♀♀♀

♒

viernes
17

☽✶♅   1:59 am
☽✶♀   6:51 am
☉✶♄   8:05 am
☽☌♂   8:53 pm
☉✶☽   9:56 pm
☽□♀   10:28 pm

___

All aspects in Pacific Standard Time; add 3 hours for EST; add 8 hours for GMT

Elves in Malibu

Devas do not usually enter busy cities
but are in lakes, streams, brooks, marshes and oceans
and can be as large as the mountains they inhabit.
The Deva of Mt. Rainier, state of Washington,
incarnated six times in an attempt to understand human feeling.
Of course, their primary state is a vortex
of nebulous lights and colors or liquid gold.
Angels of nature keep the earth green and growing.

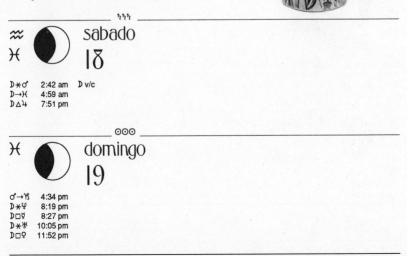

Tree Spirit Vessel
❂ *Bev Severn 1989*

You can only see them when they let you.
A current expert advises: don't try too hard,
but if you think of an entity,
    you'll be in contact.
They are presently limited
    in their power by disbelief
but warn us not to think
    we can do without them.
Further advice:
    go to the mountains for reverence,
the lakes for peace,
    and the desert for keenness of mind.

excerpt, ❂ Starr Goode

♒︎
♓︎ 🌓 sabado
18

☽✶♂ 2:42 am ☽ v/c
☽→♓ 4:59 am
☽△♃ 7:51 pm

♓︎ 🌓 domingo
19

♂→♑ 4:34 pm
☽✶♆ 8:19 pm
☽□♅ 8:27 pm
☽✶♅ 10:05 pm
☽□♀ 11:52 pm

December
ⅅⅅⅅ

♓ ☽ Monday
♈   20

☽△♀ 9:40 am
☉□☽ 2:27 pm ☽ v/c
☽→♈ 4:19 pm
☽□♂ 5:56 pm

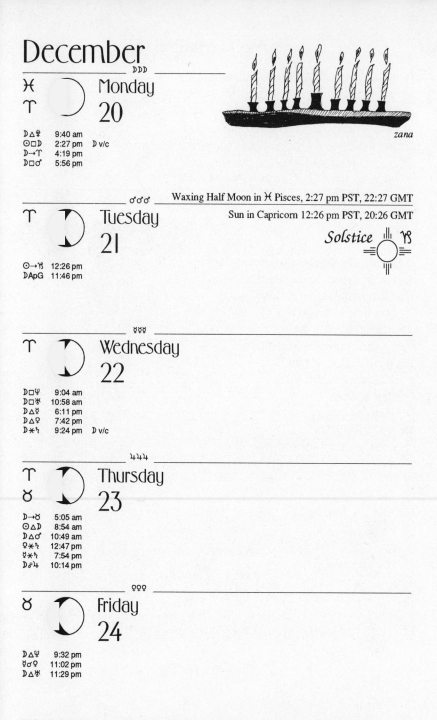

zana

♂♂♂

♈ ☽ Tuesday
       21

☉→♑ 12:26 pm
☽ApG 11:46 pm

Waxing Half Moon in ♓ Pisces, 2:27 pm PST, 22:27 GMT
Sun in Capricorn 12:26 pm PST, 20:26 GMT

Solstice ♑

☿☿☿

♈ ☽ Wednesday
       22

☽□♆ 9:04 am
☽□♅ 10:58 am
☽△♅ 6:11 pm
☽△♀ 7:42 pm
☽✳♄ 9:24 am ☽ v/c

♃♃♃

♈ ☽ Thursday
♉   23

☽→♉ 5:05 am
☉△☽ 8:54 am
☽△♂ 10:49 am
♀✳♄ 12:47 pm
☿✳♄ 7:54 pm
☽☌♃ 10:14 pm

♀♀♀

♉ ☽ Friday
       24

☽△♆ 9:32 pm
☿☌♀ 11:02 pm
☽△♅ 11:29 pm

All aspects in Pacific Standard Time; add 3 hours for EST; add 8 hours for GMT

Winter Solstice   © Sudie Rakusin 1991

Cleansing Ceremony On Winter Solstice

Spirits of the East we invoke you, we call we call.
Oh Inanna, bring your windbreath of clarity.
Come back come back from your journey to the Great Below
and with your sweet fresh breeze
gently blow our confusion away.
Watchers and ancestors and animals of the East
be welcome to our sacred Circle.

Spirits of the South we invoke you, we call we call.
Oh Kali, Queen of fire and rages,
bring us courage to destroy
that which needs to be destroyed.
Illumine illumine the truth in us.
Watchers and ancestors and animals of the South
be welcome to our sacred Circle.

Spirits of the West, we invoke you, we call we call.
Oh Mara, with your waters wash away from us
our grief and shame and fear.
Bathe us in our own innocence.
Watchers and ancestors and animals of the West
be welcome to our sacred Circle.

Spirits of the North, we invoke you, we call we call.
Hecate, Mother of the Longest Night.
give us your grounding, your deep winter dreaming.
Guardian of the Crossroads,
bring to us your green child of hope.
Watchers and ancestors and animals of the North
be welcome to our sacred Circle.

Sue Silvermarie

Standing alone on the steps of the church I look into clouds. I listen to the songs of angels. I feel the breeze of dead souls who move through me to green hills. Golden halls that have no end circle endlessly with painted ceilings. I am lost among pillars carved with the spirals of my life.

❂ *V.S. Sekhmet*

ᚻᚻᚻ

♉
♊

Saturday
25

☽□♄   9:47 am
☽☍♀   10:39 am   ☽ v/c
☽→♊   4:46 pm

☉☉☉

♊

Sunday
26

♉→♑   4:47 am
♀→♑   12:10 pm
☉♂♂   6:29 pm

Dezember

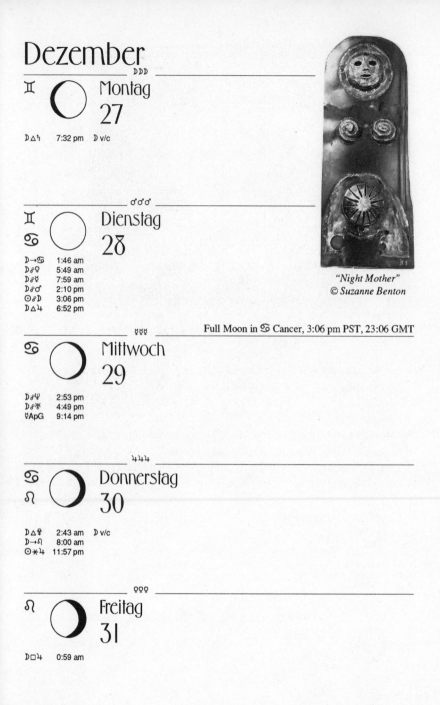

DDD _____

♊ 🌑 **Montag**
27

D△ħ   7:32 pm   D v/c

♂♂♂ _____

♊
♋ 🌕 **Dienstag**
28

D→♋   1:46 am
D☍♀   5:49 am
D☍♅   7:59 am
D☍♂   2:10 pm
☉☍D   3:06 pm
D△♃   6:52 pm

"Night Mother"
© *Suzanne Benton*

☿☿☿ _____

Full Moon in ♋ Cancer, 3:06 pm PST, 23:06 GMT

♋ 🌗 **Mittwoch**
29

D☍Ψ   2:53 pm
D☍♅   4:49 pm
☿ApG   9:14 pm

♃♃♃ _____

♋
♌ 🌒 **Donnerstag**
30

D△♀   2:43 am   D v/c
D→♌   8:00 am
☉⚹♃   11:57 pm

♀♀♀ _____

♌ 🌑 **Freitag**
31

D□♃   0:59 am

_____

All aspects in Pacific Standard Time; add 3 hours for EST; add 8 hours for GMT

HAZEL (Corylus spp.)

Hazel is often associated with the fairy world. Many
different spells for seeing the fey folk involve using
different parts of the hazel tree. A wreath of the young
branches placed on the head is a great way to open
yourself to the world of nature spirits. So is sitting very
still under the hazel tree. Sacred to Artemis, Diana and
Morgan Le Fey.

© *Colette Gardiner 1992*

♌ ♍	◗	Samstag 1	Januar, 1994

☿♂♂ 3:37 am
☽☍♄ 7:12 am
☽☐♀ 7:15 am
☿⚹♃ 10:09 am   ☽ v/c
☽→♍ 12:15 pm
♄☐♀ 6:56 pm
♂⚹♃ 7:08 pm

♍	◗	Sonntag 2

☽△♀ 2:30 am
☽⚹♃ 5:24 am
☽△♂ 5:53 am
☽△♅ 7:39 am
☉△☽ 8:58 am
☽△♆ 11:25 pm

janvier

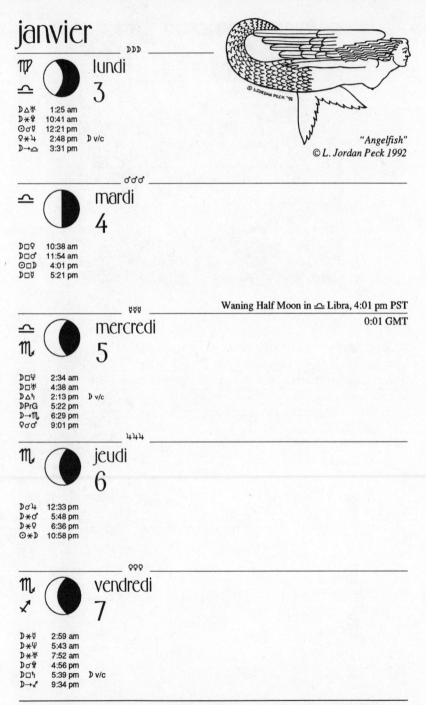

DDD

♍︎
♎︎ lundi
3

D△♅	1:25 am
D✶♀	10:41 am
☉♂♅	12:21 pm
♀✶♃	2:48 pm	D v/c
D→♎︎	3:31 pm

"Angelfish"
© L. Jordan Peck 1992

♂♂♂

♎︎ mardi
4

D□♀	10:38 am
D□♂	11:54 am
☉□D	4:01 pm
D□♅	5:21 pm

☿☿☿

Waning Half Moon in ♎︎ Libra, 4:01 pm PST
0:01 GMT

♎︎
♏︎ mercredi
5

D□♆	2:34 am
D□♅	4:38 am
D△♄	2:13 pm	D v/c
DPrG	5:22 pm
D→♏︎	6:29 pm
♀☌♂	9:01 pm

♃♃♃

♏︎ jeudi
6

D☌♃	12:33 pm
D✶♂	5:48 pm
D✶♀	6:36 pm
☉✶D	10:58 pm

♀♀♀

♏︎
♐︎ vendredi
7

D✶♅	2:59 am
D✶♆	5:43 am
D✶♅	7:52 am
D☌♀	4:56 pm
D□♄	5:39 pm	D v/c
D→♐︎	9:34 pm

All aspects in Pacific Standard Time; add 3 hours for EST; add 8 hours for GMT

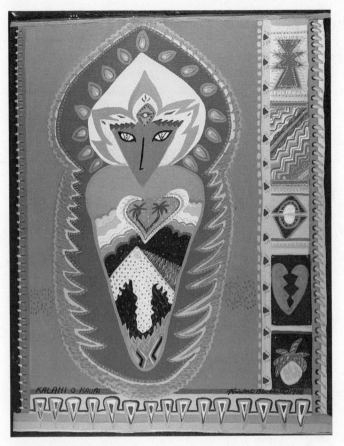

Kalani O Kauai   © *A. Kimberlin Blackburn 1988*

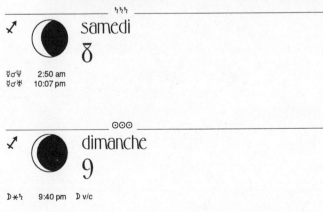

♐ samedi
8

☿☌♆   2:50 am
☿☌♅   10:07 pm

♐ dimanche
9

☽⚹♄   9:40 pm   ☽ v/c

enero

☽☽☽

♐
♑
lunes
10

☽→♑   1:16 am
☽✳♃   8:56 pm
☉☌♆   11:33 pm

♂♂♂

♑
martes
11

♆ApG   1:24 am
☽☌♂   7:32 am
☽☌♀   12:46 pm
☽☌♆   2:02 pm
☉☌☽   3:11 pm
☽☌♅   4:28 pm

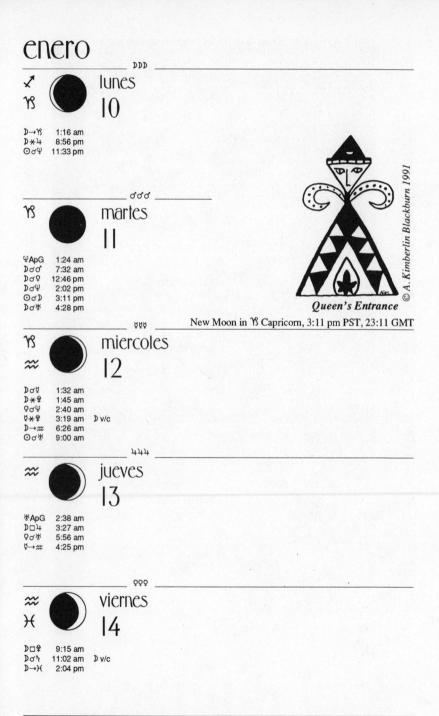

Queen's Entrance

© A. Kimberlin Blackburn 1991

New Moon in ♑ Capricorn, 3:11 pm PST, 23:11 GMT

☿☿☿

♑
♒
miercoles
12

☽☌♅   1:32 am
☽✳♀   1:45 am
♀☌♆   2:40 am
☿✳♀   3:19 am   ☽ v/c
☽→♒   6:26 am
☉☌♅   9:00 am

♃♃♃

♒
jueves
13

♅ApG   2:38 am
☽□♃   3:27 am
♀☌♅   5:56 am
☿→♒   4:25 pm

♀♀♀

♒
♓
viernes
14

☽□♀   9:15 am
☽☌♄   11:02 am   ☽ v/c
☽→♓   2:04 pm

All aspects in Pacific Standard Time; add 3 hours for EST; add 8 hours for GMT

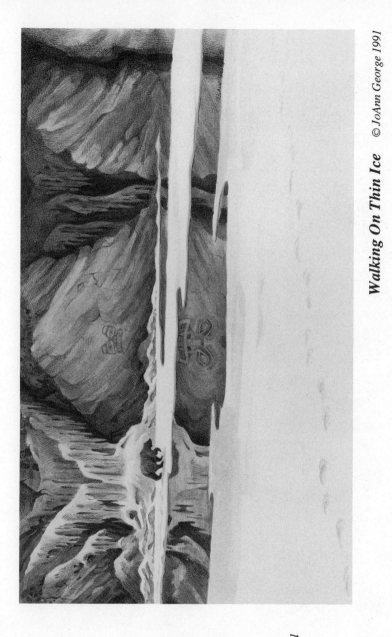

Walking On Thin Ice © *JoAnn George 1991*

Prayer

Mother of All
thank you

She Who
calls my name
and I come
running

✿ *Shemaya*
Mountain Laurel

January - Januar - Janvier - enero

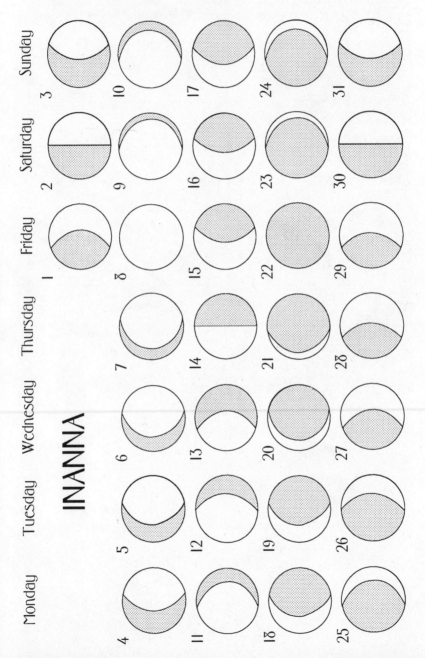

INANNA

Sunday: 3, 10, 17, 24, 31
Saturday: 2, 9, 16, 23, 30
Friday: 1, 8, 15, 22, 29
Thursday: 7, 14, 21, 28
Wednesday: 6, 13, 20, 27
Tuesday: 5, 12, 19, 26
Monday: 4, 11, 18, 25

February - Februar - fevrier - febrero

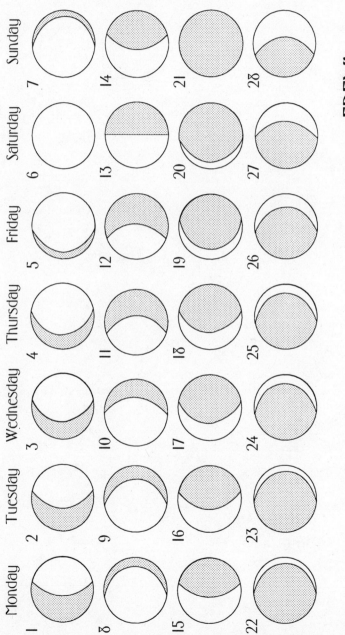

FREYA

Sunday 7 14 21 28
Saturday 6 13 20 27
Friday 5 12 19 26
Thursday 4 11 18 25
Wednesday 3 10 17 24
Tuesday 2 9 16 23
Monday 1 8 15 22

March - Marz - mars - marzo

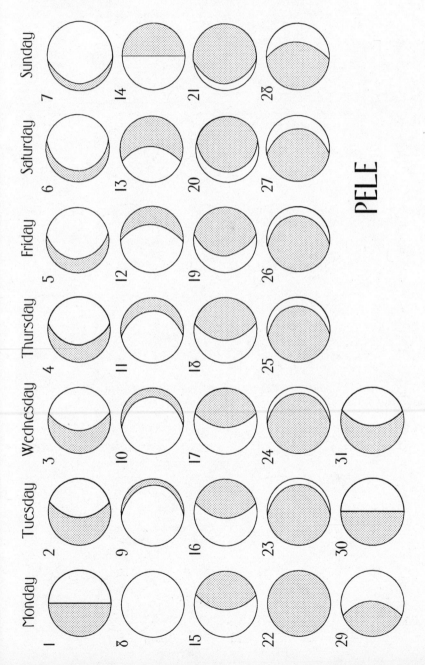

PELE

April - April - avril - abril

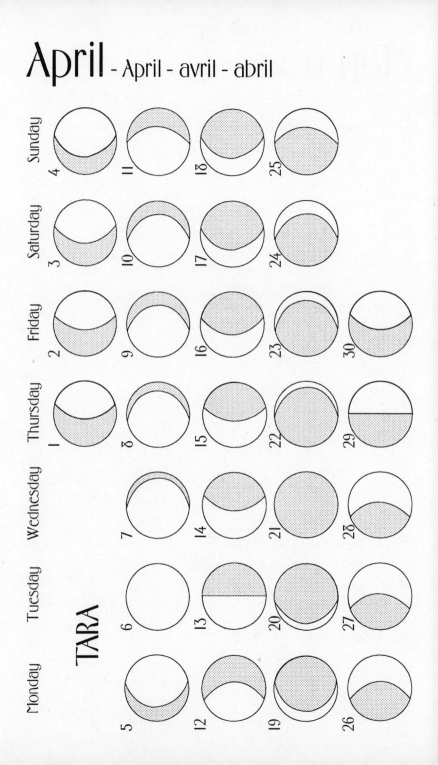

TARA

Monday
Tuesday
Wednesday
Thursday
Friday
Saturday
Sunday

1
2
3
4
5
6
7
8
9
10
11
12
13
14
15
16
17
18
19
20
21
22
23
24
25
26
27
28
29
30

May - Mai - mai - mayo

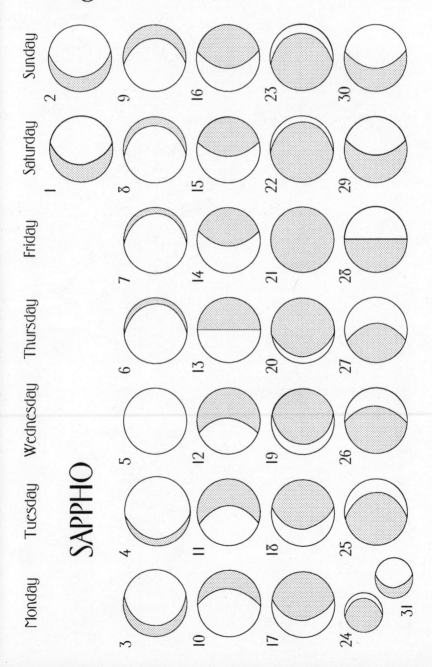

SAPPHO

Monday	Tuesday	Wednesday	Thursday	Friday	Saturday	Sunday
					1	2
3	4	5	6	7	8	9
10	11	12	13	14	15	16
17	18	19	20	21	22	23
24	25	26	27	28	29	30
31						

June - Juni - juin - junio

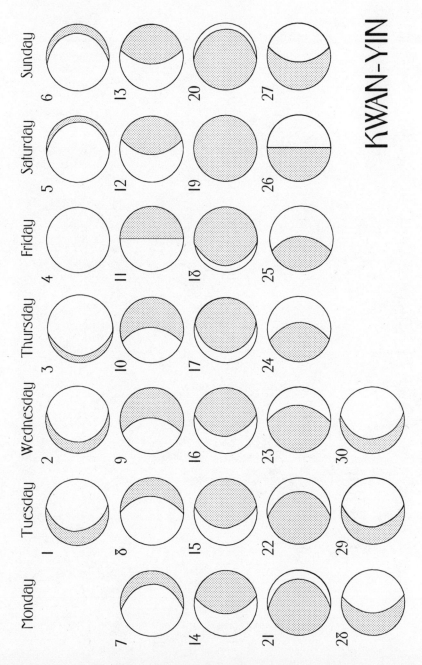

KWAN-YIN

Sunday 6 | 13 | 20 | 27

Saturday 5 | 12 | 19 | 26

Friday 4 | 11 | 18 | 25

Thursday 3 | 10 | 17 | 24

Wednesday 2 | 9 | 16 | 23 | 30

Tuesday 1 | 8 | 15 | 22 | 29

Monday 7 | 14 | 21 | 28

July - Juli - juilliet - julio

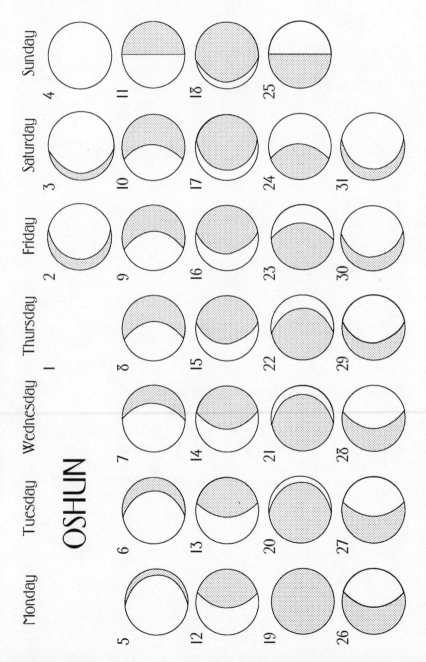

Sunday 4 11 18 25

Saturday 3 10 17 24 31

Friday 2 9 16 23 30

Thursday 1 8 15 22 29

Wednesday 7 14 21 28

Tuesday OSHUN 6 13 20 27

Monday 5 12 19 26

August - August - aout - agosto

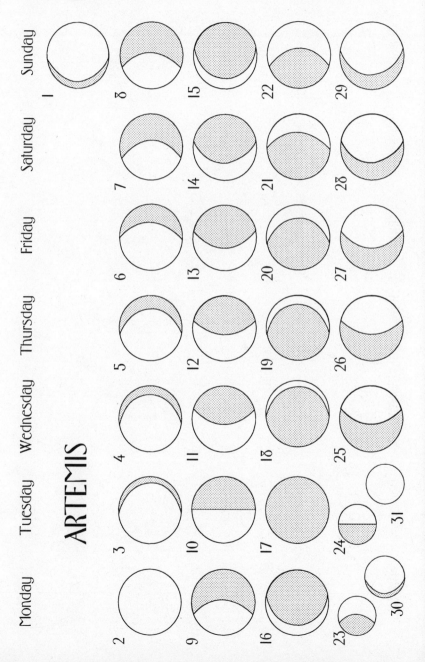

September-septembre-septiembre

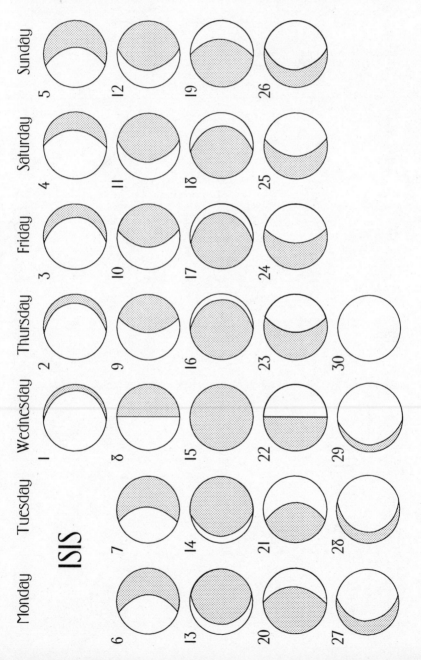

ISIS

Sunday 5, 12, 19, 26
Saturday 4, 11, 18, 25
Friday 3, 10, 17, 24
Thursday 2, 9, 16, 23, 30
Wednesday 1, 8, 15, 22, 29
Tuesday 7, 14, 21, 28
Monday 6, 13, 20, 27

October - Oktober - octobre - octubre

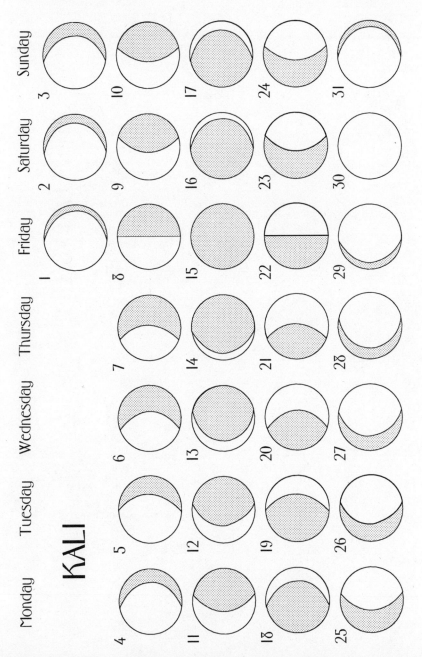

Sunday
3
10
17
24
31

Saturday
2
9
16
23
30

Friday
1
8
15
22
29

Thursday
7
14
21
28

Wednesday
6
13
20
27

Tuesday
5
12
19
26

Monday
4
11
18
25

KALI

November -novembre-noviembre

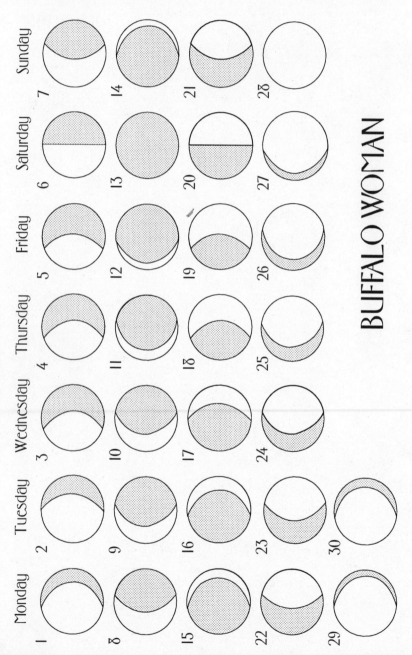

Monday   Tuesday   Wednesday   Thursday   Friday   Saturday   Sunday

1   2   3   4   5   6   7

8   9   10   11   12   13   14

15   16   17   18   19   20   21

22   23   24   25   26   27   28

29   30

BUFFALO WOMAN

December - Dezember - decembre

diciembre

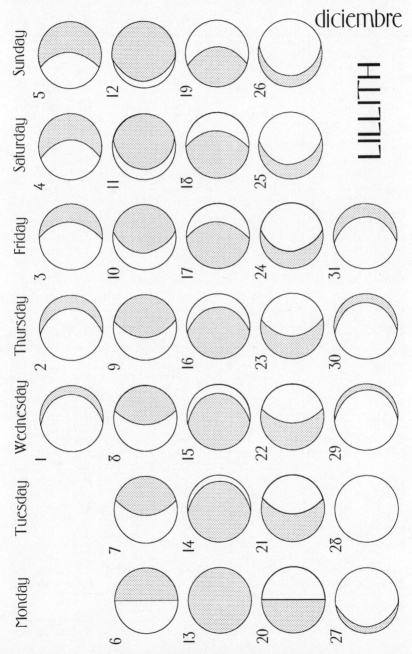

LILLITH

NOON EPHEMERIS: GMT* JANUARY 1993

Day	☉	Noon ☽	True ☊	☿	♀	♂	♃	♄	♅	♆	♇
1 F	11♑ 5 45	14♈56 46	21♐19.0	28♐18.2	27♒14.2	20♋13.4	13♎31.6	16♒24.2	17♑41.9	18♑22.5	24♏37.2
2 Sa	12 6 54	27 9 51	21D19.8	29 49.4	28 20.8	19R49.9	13 36.5	16 30.6	17 45.5	18 24.7	24 39.0
3 Su	13 8 3	9♉39 30	21 21.1	1♑20.9	29 27.2	19 26.2	13 41.2	16 37.0	17 49.1	18 27.0	24 40.8
4 M	14 9 12	22 29 49	21 22.8	2 52.9	0♓33.3	19 2.4	13 45.8	16 43.4	17 52.6	18 29.3	24 42.6
5 Tu	15 10 20	5♊43 53	21 24.1	4 25.2	1 39.2	18 38.5	13 50.1	16 49.9	17 56.2	18 31.6	24 44.3
6 W	16 11 28	19 23 12	21R24.8	5 58.0	2 44.8	18 14.5	13 54.4	16 56.4	17 59.8	18 33.8	24 46.0
7 Th	17 12 36	3♋27 8	21 24.2	7 31.1	3 50.1	17 50.6	13 58.4	17 3.0	18 3.3	18 36.1	24 47.7
8 F	18 13 44	17 52 40	21 22.4	9 4.6	4 55.2	17 26.6	14 2.3	17 9.6	18 6.9	18 38.4	24 49.3
9 Sa	19 14 51	2♌34 19	21 19.3	10 38.5	5 60.0	17 2.8	14 6.0	17 16.3	18 10.5	18 40.7	24 51.0
10 Su	20 15 58	17 24 44	21 15.2	12 12.8	7 4.4	16 39.2	14 9.5	17 23.0	18 14.0	18 42.9	24 52.6
11 M	21 17 5	2♍15 42	21 10.8	13 47.6	8 8.6	16 15.7	14 12.9	17 29.7	18 17.6	18 45.2	24 54.1
12 Tu	22 18 12	16 59 28	21 6.8	15 22.8	9 12.4	15 52.5	14 16.1	17 36.4	18 21.2	18 47.5	24 55.7
13 W	23 19 19	1♎29 47	21 3.7	16 58.5	10 16.0	15 29.5	14 19.1	17 43.2	18 24.7	18 49.8	24 57.2
14 Th	24 20 25	15 42 37	21 2.0	18 34.7	11 19.1	15 6.9	14 21.9	17 50.0	18 28.3	18 52.0	24 58.7
15 F	25 21 32	29 36 9	21D 1.7	20 11.4	12 22.0	14 44.6	14 24.5	17 56.9	18 31.8	18 54.3	25 0.1
16 Sa	26 22 38	13♏10 28	21 2.6	21 48.5	13 24.5	14 22.7	14 27.0	18 3.7	18 35.4	18 56.6	25 1.5
17 Su	27 23 45	26 26 52	21 4.2	23 26.2	14 26.6	14 1.3	14 29.2	18 10.6	18 38.9	18 58.8	25 2.9
18 M	28 24 51	9♐27 23	21 5.5	25 4.4	15 28.4	13 40.3	14 31.3	18 17.6	18 42.5	19 1.1	25 4.3
19 Tu	29 25 56	22 14 6	21R 6.0	26 43.2	16 29.8	13 19.9	14 33.2	18 24.5	18 46.0	19 3.3	25 5.6
20 W	0♒27 2	4♑48 59	21 4.8	28 22.5	17 30.7	13 0.0	14 34.9	18 31.5	18 49.5	19 5.6	25 7.0
21 Th	1 28 6	17 13 37	21 1.6	0♒ 2.4	18 31.3	12 40.8	14 36.4	18 38.5	18 53.0	19 7.8	25 8.2
22 F	2 29 10	29 29 18	20 56.3	1 42.9	19 31.4	12 22.1	14 37.8	18 45.6	18 56.6	19 10.0	25 9.5
23 Sa	3 30 14	11♒37 7	20 49.1	3 24.0	20 31.0	12 4.1	14 38.9	18 52.6	19 0.0	19 12.3	25 10.7
24 Su	4 31 16	23 38 10	20 40.6	5 5.7	21 30.2	11 46.8	14 39.8	18 59.7	19 3.5	19 14.5	25 11.8
25 M	5 32 18	5♓33 49	20 31.6	6 48.0	22 28.9	11 30.1	14 40.6	19 6.8	19 7.0	19 16.7	25 13.0
26 Tu	6 33 18	17 25 52	20 22.9	8 30.8	23 27.1	11 14.2	14 41.2	19 13.9	19 10.4	19 18.9	25 14.1
27 W	7 34 18	29 16 44	20 15.4	10 14.3	24 24.8	10 59.1	14 41.5	19 21.0	19 13.9	19 21.1	25 15.2
28 Th	8 35 16	11♈ 9 33	20 9.6	11 58.3	25 21.9	10 44.6	14R41.7	19 28.2	19 17.3	19 23.3	25 16.2
29 F	9 36 13	23 8 9	20 5.9	13 42.9	26 18.5	10 31.0	14 41.7	19 35.3	19 20.7	19 25.4	25 17.2
30 Sa	10 37 10	5♉16 56	20D 4.3	15 28.1	27 14.5	10 18.1	14 41.5	19 42.5	19 24.1	19 27.6	25 18.2
31 Su	11 38 4	17 40 44	20 4.4	17 13.7	28 9.8	10 6.0	14 41.1	19 49.7	19 27.5	19 29.7	25 19.1

LONGITUDE FEBRUARY 1993

Day	☉	Noon ☽	True ☊	☿	♀	♂	♃	♄	♅	♆	♇
1 M	12♒38 58	0♊24 27	20♐ 5.3	18♒59.8	29♓ 4.5	9♋54.8	14♎40.6	19♒56.9	19♑30.9	19♑31.9	25♏20.0
2 Tu	13 39 50	13 32 34	20R 6.2	20 46.3	29 58.6	9R44.3	14R39.8	20 4.1	19 34.2	19 34.0	25 20.9
3 W	14 40 41	27 8 26	20 6.0	22 33.0	0♈52.0	9 34.6	14 38.8	20 11.3	19 37.5	19 36.1	25 21.8
4 Th	15 41 31	11♋13 28	20 3.9	24 20.0	1 44.7	9 25.8	14 37.7	20 18.5	19 40.8	19 38.2	25 22.6
5 F	16 42 19	25 46 17	19 59.4	26 7.0	2 36.6	9 17.7	14 36.4	20 25.7	19 44.1	19 40.3	25 23.3
6 Sa	17 43 6	10♌42 5	19 52.6	27 54.0	3 27.8	9 10.4	14 34.8	20 32.9	19 47.4	19 42.4	25 24.1
7 Su	18 43 51	25 52 46	19 44.0	29 40.8	4 18.1	9 4.0	14 33.1	20 40.1	19 50.6	19 44.4	25 24.8
8 M	19 44 36	11♍ 7 49	19 34.5	1♓27.1	5 7.6	8 58.3	14 31.2	20 47.4	19 53.9	19 46.5	25 25.4
9 Tu	20 45 19	26 16 14	19 25.4	3 12.8	5 56.3	8 53.4	14 29.1	20 54.6	19 57.0	19 48.5	25 26.1
10 W	21 46 1	11♎ 8 24	19 17.7	4 57.5	6 44.1	8 49.4	14 26.9	21 1.8	20 0.2	19 50.5	25 26.7
11 Th	22 46 42	25 37 35	19 12.2	6 40.9	7 31.0	8 46.1	14 24.4	21 9.1	20 3.4	19 52.5	25 27.2
12 F	23 47 22	9♏40 30	19 9.1	8 22.6	8 16.9	8 43.5	14 21.8	21 16.3	20 6.5	19 54.5	25 27.7
13 Sa	24 48 0	23 16 57	19D 8.1	10 2.2	9 1.8	8 41.8	14 18.9	21 23.5	20 9.6	19 56.4	25 28.2
14 Su	25 48 38	6♐29 2	19 8.3	11 39.2	9 45.7	8 40.8	14 15.9	21 30.8	20 12.7	19 58.4	25 28.7
15 M	26 49 15	19 20 8	19R 8.7	13 13.1	10 28.6	8D40.5	14 12.8	21 38.0	20 15.7	20 0.3	25 29.1
16 Tu	27 49 50	1♑54 9	19 8.1	14 43.4	11 10.3	8 41.0	14 9.4	21 45.2	20 18.8	20 2.2	25 29.5
17 W	28 50 24	14 14 54	19 5.3	16 9.3	11 50.9	8 42.3	14 5.9	21 52.4	20 21.7	20 4.1	25 29.8
18 Th	29 50 57	26 25 43	18 59.7	17 30.3	12 30.3	8 44.3	14 2.1	21 59.6	20 24.7	20 6.0	25 30.1
19 F	0♓51 29	8♒29 22	18 51.1	18 45.7	13 8.4	8 46.9	13 58.2	22 6.8	20 27.6	20 7.8	25 30.4
20 Sa	1 51 58	20 27 54	18 39.8	19 54.8	13 45.2	8 50.3	13 54.2	22 14.0	20 30.6	20 9.6	25 30.7
21 Su	2 52 27	2♓22 55	18 26.5	20 56.9	14 20.7	8 54.4	13 50.0	22 21.1	20 33.4	20 11.4	25 30.9
22 M	3 52 53	14 15 42	18 12.2	21 51.4	14 54.9	8 59.2	13 45.6	22 28.3	20 36.3	20 13.2	25 31.0
23 Tu	4 53 18	26 7 30	17 58.1	22 37.7	15 27.5	9 4.7	13 41.0	22 35.4	20 39.1	20 15.0	25 31.2
24 W	5 53 42	7♈59 51	17 45.3	23 15.3	15 58.6	9 10.8	13 36.3	22 42.5	20 41.9	20 16.7	25 31.2
25 Th	6 54 3	19 54 44	17 34.9	23 43.7	16 28.2	9 17.6	13 31.4	22 49.6	20 44.6	20 18.4	25 31.3
26 F	7 54 22	1♉54 49	17 27.4	24 2.7	16 56.1	9 25.0	13 26.4	22 56.7	20 47.3	20 20.1	25R31.3
27 Sa	8 54 40	14 3 30	17 22.8	24R12.0	17 22.4	9 33.1	13 21.2	23 3.8	20 50.0	20 21.8	25 31.3
28 Su	9 54 56	26 24 50	17 20.8	24 11.5	17 46.8	9 41.8	13 15.9	23 10.8	20 52.6	20 23.4	25 31.3

Reprinted with permission from Astro-Computing Services

* giving the positions of planets daily at noon, Greenwich Mean Time

NOON EPHEMERIS: GMT* MARCH 1993

Day	☉	Noon ☽	True ☊	☿	♀	♂	♃	♄	♅	♆	♇
1 M	10♓55 9	9♊ 3 24	17♐20.4	24♓ 1.5	18♈ 9.5	9♋51.0	13♎10.4	23♒17.8	20♑55.2	20♑25.0	25♏31.2
2 Tu	11 55 21	22 3 51	17R20.4	23R42.2	18 30.2	10 0.9	13R 4.8	23 24.9	20 57.8	20 26.6	25R31.1
3 W	12 55 31	5♋30 23	17 19.6	23 14.3	18 49.0	10 11.3	12 59.0	23 31.8	21 0.3	20 28.2	25 30.9
4 Th	13 55 38	19 25 52	17 16.8	22 38.3	19 5.8	10 22.3	12 53.2	23 38.8	21 2.8	20 29.8	25 30.7
5 F	14 55 43	3♌50 49	17 11.4	21 55.2	19 20.5	10 33.9	12 47.2	23 45.7	21 5.3	20 31.3	25 30.5
6 Sa	15 55 46	18 42 28	17 3.2	21 6.2	19 33.0	10 46.0	12 41.0	23 52.6	21 7.7	20 32.8	25 30.2
7 Su	16 55 48	3♍54 14	16 52.9	20 12.4	19 43.3	10 58.6	12 34.8	23 59.5	21 10.1	20 34.2	25 29.9
8 M	17 55 47	19 16 10	16 41.4	19 15.2	19 51.3	11 11.7	12 28.4	24 6.3	21 12.4	20 35.7	25 29.6
9 Tu	18 55 44	4♎36 22	16 30.1	18 16.0	19 57.1	11 25.3	12 21.9	24 13.1	21 14.7	20 37.1	25 29.3
10 W	19 55 39	19 43 17	16 20.3	17 16.1	20 0.4	11 39.4	12 15.3	24 19.9	21 17.0	20 38.5	25 28.9
11 Th	20 55 33	4♏27 44	16 12.8	16 17.0	20R 1.4	11 54.0	12 8.6	24 26.7	21 19.2	20 39.8	25 28.4
12 F	21 55 25	18 44 11	16 7.5	15 19.8	19 59.9	12 9.1	12 1.8	24 33.4	21 21.4	20 41.2	25 28.0
13 Sa	22 55 16	2♐30 50	16 5.8	14 25.7	19 55.9	12 24.6	11 54.9	24 40.1	21 23.6	20 42.5	25 27.5
14 Su	23 55 4	15 48 57	16D 5.3	13 35.5	19 49.5	12 40.5	11 48.0	24 46.7	21 25.7	20 43.7	25 27.0
15 M	24 54 52	28 41 53	16R 5.3	12 50.2	19 40.6	12 56.9	11 40.9	24 53.3	21 27.7	20 45.0	25 26.4
16 Tu	25 54 37	11♑14 2	16 4.7	12 10.2	19 29.2	13 13.7	11 33.7	24 59.9	21 29.7	20 46.2	25 25.8
17 W	26 54 21	23 30 12	16 2.2	11 36.0	19 15.3	13 31.0	11 26.5	25 6.4	21 31.7	20 47.4	25 25.2
18 Th	27 54 3	5♒34 52	15 57.1	11 7.9	18 59.0	13 48.6	11 19.2	25 12.9	21 33.6	20 48.6	25 24.5
19 F	28 53 43	17 32 4	15 49.1	10 46.0	18 40.3	14 6.7	11 11.8	25 19.4	21 35.5	20 49.7	25 23.8
20 Sa	29 53 21	29 25 6	15 38.3	10 30.4	18 19.3	14 25.2	11 4.4	25 25.8	21 37.4	20 50.8	25 23.1
21 Su	0♈52 57	11♓16 32	15 25.6	10 20.9	17 56.0	14 44.0	10 56.9	25 32.2	21 39.2	20 51.9	25 22.4
22 M	1 52 32	23 8 20	15 11.7	10D17.5	17 30.5	15 3.2	10 49.4	25 38.5	21 40.9	20 52.9	25 21.6
23 Tu	2 52 4	5♈ 2 0	14 57.9	10 20.0	17 3.0	15 22.8	10 41.8	25 44.8	21 42.6	20 53.9	25 20.8
24 W	3 51 34	16 58 48	14 45.2	10 28.1	16 33.6	15 42.8	10 34.2	25 51.0	21 44.3	20 54.9	25 19.9
25 Th	4 51 3	29 0 6	14 34.8	10 41.7	16 2.4	16 3.1	10 26.5	25 57.2	21 45.9	20 55.8	25 19.1
26 F	5 50 29	11♉ 7 33	14 27.2	11 0.4	15 29.6	16 23.7	10 18.8	26 3.3	21 47.4	20 56.7	25 18.2
27 Sa	6 49 53	23 23 19	14 22.5	11 24.1	14 55.4	16 44.7	10 11.1	26 9.4	21 48.9	20 57.6	25 17.2
28 Su	7 49 15	5♊50 11	14 20.5	11 52.4	14 20.0	17 6.1	10 3.4	26 15.5	21 50.4	20 58.5	25 16.3
29 M	8 48 34	18 31 29	14D20.4	12 25.0	13 43.7	17 27.7	9 55.7	26 21.4	21 51.8	20 59.3	25 15.3
30 Tu	9 47 51	1♋30 53	14 21.1	13 1.9	13 6.6	17 49.7	9 47.9	26 27.4	21 53.2	21 0.1	25 14.3
31 W	10 47 6	14 51 58	14R21.3	13 42.6	12 29.0	18 11.9	9 40.2	26 33.3	21 54.5	21 0.8	25 13.3

LONGITUDE APRIL 1993

Day	☉	Noon ☽	True ☊	☿	♀	♂	♃	♄	♅	♆	♇
1 Th	11♈46 19	28♋37 38	14♐20.1	14♓27.1	11♈51.1	18♋34.5	9♎32.4	26♒39.1	21♑55.8	21♑ 1.6	25♏12.2
2 F	12 45 29	12♌49 10	14R16.6	15 15.1	11R13.3	18 57.4	9R24.7	26 44.8	21 57.0	21 2.2	25R11.1
3 Sa	13 44 37	27 25 24	14 10.9	16 6.3	10 35.7	19 20.5	9 17.0	26 50.6	21 58.2	21 2.9	25 10.0
4 Su	14 43 42	12♍22 0	14 3.2	17 0.7	9 58.6	19 43.9	9 9.3	26 56.2	21 59.3	21 3.5	25 8.9
5 M	15 42 46	27 31 25	13 54.4	17 58.1	9 22.3	20 7.6	9 1.7	27 1.8	22 0.4	21 4.1	25 7.7
6 Tu	16 41 47	12♎43 45	13 45.6	18 58.3	8 47.0	20 31.5	8 54.0	27 7.3	22 1.4	21 4.7	25 6.5
7 W	17 40 46	27 48 16	13 37.9	20 1.2	8 12.9	20 55.7	8 46.4	27 12.8	22 2.4	21 5.2	25 5.3
8 Th	18 39 43	12♏35 22	13 32.1	21 6.7	7 40.3	21 20.1	8 38.9	27 18.2	22 3.4	21 5.7	25 4.1
9 F	19 38 38	26 58 6	13 28.6	22 14.6	7 9.2	21 44.8	8 31.4	27 23.6	22 4.2	21 6.2	25 2.8
10 Sa	20 37 30	10♐52 50	13D27.3	23 24.9	6 40.0	22 9.7	8 24.0	27 28.9	22 5.1	21 6.6	25 1.5
11 Su	21 36 24	24 19 4	13 27.6	24 37.4	6 12.7	22 34.9	8 16.6	27 34.1	22 5.9	21 7.0	25 0.2
12 M	22 35 14	7♑18 49	13 28.7	25 52.2	5 47.5	23 0.3	8 9.2	27 39.3	22 6.6	21 7.4	24 58.9
13 Tu	23 34 1	19 55 44	13R29.6	27 9.0	5 24.5	23 25.9	8 2.0	27 44.4	22 7.3	21 7.7	24 57.6
14 W	24 32 49	2♒14 23	13 29.4	28 27.9	5 3.7	23 51.8	7 54.8	27 49.4	22 7.9	21 8.0	24 56.2
15 Th	25 31 34	14 19 34	13 27.4	29 48.7	4 45.3	24 17.8	7 47.7	27 54.4	22 8.5	21 8.3	24 54.8
16 F	26 30 17	26 15 59	13 23.3	1♈11.5	4 29.3	24 44.1	7 40.6	27 59.3	22 9.0	21 8.5	24 53.4
17 Sa	27 28 58	8♓ 7 53	13 17.4	2 36.2	4 15.7	25 10.6	7 33.7	28 4.1	22 9.5	21 8.7	24 52.0
18 Su	28 • 27 38	19 58 53	13 9.9	4 2.7	4 4.6	25 37.3	7 26.8	28 8.8	22 9.9	21 8.8	24 50.6
19 M	29 26 16	1♈51 58	13 1.6	5 31.1	3 55.9	26 4.2	7 20.1	28 13.5	22 10.3	21 9.0	24 49.1
20 Tu	0♉24 52	13 49 30	12 53.2	7 1.2	3 49.7	26 31.2	7 13.4	28 18.1	22 10.6	21 9.1	24 47.7
21 W	1 23 26	25 53 13	12 45.5	8 33.2	3 45.9	26 58.5	7 6.9	28 22.7	22 10.9	21 9.1	24 46.2
22 Th	2 21 58	8♉ 4 31	12 39.3	10 6.9	3D44.5	27 26.0	7 0.4	28 27.1	22 11.1	21R 9.2	24 44.7
23 F	3 20 29	20 24 34	12 35.0	11 42.3	3 45.4	27 53.7	6 54.1	28 31.5	22 11.3	21 9.2	24 43.2
24 Sa	4 18 57	2♊54 34	12 32.7	13 19.5	3 48.7	28 21.5	6 47.9	28 35.8	22 11.4	21 9.1	24 41.6
25 Su	5 17 24	15 35 53	12D32.3	14 58.4	3 54.2	28 49.6	6 41.8	28 40.1	22 11.5	21 9.1	24 40.1
26 M	6 15 48	28 30 9	12 33.3	16 39.1	4 2.0	29 17.8	6 35.8	28 44.2	22R11.5	21 9.0	24 38.5
27 Tu	7 14 11	11♋39 14	12 34.9	18 21.5	4 11.9	29 46.1	6 30.0	28 48.3	22 11.5	21 8.8	24 37.0
28 W	8 12 33	25 5 1	12 36.4	20 5.7	4 24.0	0♌14.7	6 24.3	28 52.3	22 11.4	21 8.7	24 35.4
29 Th	9 10 49	8♌49 0	12R37.1	21 51.6	4 38.1	0 43.4	6 18.7	28 56.2	22 11.3	21 8.5	24 33.8
30 F	10 9 6	22 51 49	12 36.5	23 39.3	4 54.1	1 12.3	6 13.3	29 0.0	22 11.1	21 8.2	24 32.2

* giving the positions of planets daily at noon, Greenwich Mean Time

NOON EPHEMERIS: GMT*

MAY 1993

Day	☉	Noon ☽	True ☊	☿	♀	♂	♃	♄	♅	♆	♇
1 Sa	11♉ 7 20	7♍12 37	12♐34.5	25♈28.7	5♈12.1	1♌41.3	6♎ 8.0	29♒ 3.8	22♑10.8	21♑ 8.0	24♏30.6
2 Su	12 5 32	21 48 34	12R31.2	27 19.9	5 32.0	2 10.4	6R 2.9	29 7.4	22R10.6	21R 7.7	24R29.0
3 M	13 3 41	6♎34 43	12 27.3	29 12.9	5 53.7	2 39.8	5 57.9	29 11.0	22 10.2	21 7.3	24 27.4
4 Tu	14 1 50	21 24 18	12 23.2	1♉ 7.7	6 17.1	3 9.2	5 53.0	29 14.5	22 9.9	21 7.0	24 25.7
5 W	14 59 56	6♏ 9 32	12 19.8	3 4.2	6 42.2	3 38.8	5 48.3	29 17.9	22 9.4	21 6.6	24 24.1
6 Th	15 58 0	20 42 48	12 17.3	5 2.4	7 8.9	4 8.6	5 43.8	29 21.3	22 8.9	21 6.2	24 22.5
7 F	16 56 3	4♐57 45	12D16.2	7 2.4	7 37.2	4 38.4	5 39.4	29 24.5	22 8.4	21 5.7	24 20.8
8 Sa	17 54 5	18 50 8	12 16.3	9 4.0	8 7.1	5 8.5	5 35.2	29 27.7	22 7.9	21 5.3	24 19.2
9 Su	18 52 5	2♑18 2	12 17.3	11 7.3	8 38.4	5 38.6	5 31.1	29 30.8	22 7.2	21 4.7	24 17.5
10 M	19 50 4	15 21 44	12 18.8	13 12.1	9 11.1	6 8.9	5 27.2	29 33.7	22 6.6	21 4.2	24 15.8
11 Tu	20 48 1	28 3 21	12 20.4	15 18.2	9 45.1	6 39.3	5 23.5	29 36.6	22 5.9	21 3.6	24 14.2
12 W	21 45 57	10♒26 18	12 21.4	17 25.7	10 20.4	7 9.8	5 19.9	29 39.4	22 5.1	21 3.0	24 12.5
13 Th	22 43 51	22 34 46	12R21.8	19 34.4	10 57.0	7 40.5	5 16.5	29 42.2	22 4.3	21 2.4	24 10.8
14 F	23 41 45	4♓33 19	12 21.2	21 44.0	11 34.8	8 11.3	5 13.3	29 44.8	22 3.4	21 1.7	24 9.2
15 Sa	24 39 37	16 26 33	12 19.9	23 54.4	12 13.7	8 42.2	5 10.2	29 47.3	22 2.5	21 1.1	24 7.5
16 Su	25 37 28	28 18 52	12 17.9	26 5.4	12 53.8	9 13.2	5 7.3	29 49.8	22 1.6	21 0.3	24 5.8
17 M	26 35 17	10♈14 13	12 15.6	28 16.7	13 34.8	9 44.4	5 4.6	29 52.1	22 0.6	20 59.6	24 4.1
18 Tu	27 33 6	22 16 2	12 13.2	0♊28.0	14 16.9	10 15.6	5 2.1	29 54.4	21 59.6	20 58.8	24 2.5
19 W	28 30 53	4♉27 5	12 11.1	2 39.1	14 60.0	10 47.0	4 59.7	29 56.5	21 58.5	20 58.0	24 0.8
20 Th	29 28 39	16 49 26	12 9.6	4 49.6	15 44.0	11 18.5	4 57.5	29 58.6	21 57.3	20 57.2	23 59.1
21 F	0♊26 24	29 24 29	12 8.7	6 59.4	16 28.9	11 50.1	4 55.5	0♓ 0.6	21 56.2	20 56.3	23 57.5
22 Sa	1 24 7	12♊13 0	12D 8.5	9 8.1	17 14.7	12 21.9	4 53.7	0 2.4	21 55.0	20 55.4	23 55.8
23 Su	2 21 49	25 15 17	12 8.8	11 15.5	18 1.2	12 53.7	4 52.1	0 4.2	21 53.7	20 54.5	23 54.2
24 M	3 19 30	8♋31 12	12 9.5	13 21.3	18 48.6	13 25.6	4 50.6	0 5.9	21 52.4	20 53.6	23 52.5
25 Tu	4 17 9	22 0 22	12 10.3	15 25.4	19 36.7	13 57.7	4 49.3	0 7.5	21 51.1	20 52.6	23 50.9
26 W	5 14 47	5♌42 11	12 11.0	17 27.4	20 25.6	14 29.8	4 48.2	0 9.0	21 49.7	20 51.6	23 49.3
27 Th	6 12 23	19 35 48	12 11.5	19 27.3	21 15.2	15 2.1	4 47.3	0 10.4	21 48.3	20 50.6	23 47.6
28 F	7 9 58	3♍40 2	12R11.6	21 24.9	22 5.4	15 34.4	4 46.6	0 11.7	21 46.8	20 49.6	23 46.0
29 Sa	8 7 32	17 53 10	12 11.4	23 20.1	22 56.3	16 6.9	4 46.0	0 12.9	21 45.3	20 48.5	23 44.4
30 Su	9 5 3	2♎12 49	12 11.1	25 12.8	23 47.8	16 39.4	4 45.7	0 14.0	21 43.8	20 47.4	23 42.8
31 M	10 2 34	16 35 50	12 10.8	27 2.9	24 40.0	17 12.1	4 45.5	0 15.0	21 42.2	20 46.3	23 41.2

LONGITUDE

JUNE 1993

Day	☉	Noon ☽	True ☊	☿	♀	♂	♃	♄	♅	♆	♇
1 Tu	11♊ 0 3	0♏58 21	12♐10.6	28♊50.3	25♈32.7	17♌44.8	4♎45.5	0♓15.9	21♑40.6	20♑45.2	23♏39.6
2 W	11 57 31	15 16 0	12D10.5	0♋35.1	26 26.0	18 17.6	4D45.6	0 16.7	21R39.0	20R44.1	23R38.1
3 Th	12 54 58	29 24 18	12 10.5	2 17.1	27 19.8	18 50.5	4 46.0	0 17.4	21 37.3	20 42.9	23 36.5
4 F	13 52 24	13♐19 10	12 10.6	3 56.3	28 14.2	19 23.5	4 46.5	0 18.0	21 35.6	20 41.7	23 35.0
5 Sa	14 49 49	26 57 18	12R10.7	5 32.7	29 9.1	19 56.6	4 47.2	0 18.6	21 33.9	20 40.5	23 33.4
6 Su	15 47 14	10♑16 38	12 10.5	7 6.3	0♉ 4.5	20 29.7	4 48.1	0 19.0	21 32.1	20 39.2	23 31.9
7 M	16 44 37	23 16 28	12 10.2	8 37.0	1 0.4	21 3.0	4 49.2	0 19.3	21 30.3	20 38.0	23 30.4
8 Tu	17 42 0	5♒57 28	12 9.6	10 4.9	1 56.7	21 36.3	4 50.4	0 19.5	21 28.4	20 36.7	23 28.9
9 W	18 39 22	18 21 35	12 8.9	11 29.8	2 53.5	22 9.7	4 51.9	0 19.6	21 26.5	20 35.4	23 27.5
10 Th	19 36 43	0♓31 51	12 8.2	12 51.8	3 50.8	22 43.2	4 53.4	0R19.7	21 24.6	20 34.1	23 26.0
11 F	20 34 4	12 32 1	12 7.6	14 10.9	4 48.4	23 16.8	4 55.2	0 19.6	21 22.7	20 32.8	23 24.6
12 Sa	21 31 24	24 26 25	12D 7.4	15 26.9	5 46.4	23 50.5	4 57.2	0 19.4	21 20.7	20 31.4	23 23.1
13 Su	22 28 44	6♈19 38	12 7.5	16 39.8	6 44.9	24 24.2	4 59.3	0 19.1	21 18.7	20 30.0	23 21.7
14 M	23 26 4	18 16 14	12 8.1	17 49.6	7 43.7	24 58.1	5 1.6	0 18.8	21 16.7	20 28.6	23 20.3
15 Tu	24 23 23	0♉20 37	12 9.0	18 56.3	8 42.8	25 32.0	5 4.0	0 18.3	21 14.7	20 27.2	23 19.0
16 W	25 20 42	12 36 43	12 10.1	19 59.6	9 42.4	26 6.0	5 6.7	0 17.7	21 12.6	20 25.8	23 17.6
17 Th	26 18 0	25 7 44	12 11.2	20 59.7	10 42.2	26 40.1	5 9.5	0 17.1	21 10.5	20 24.4	23 16.3
18 F	27 15 18	7♊55 59	12 11.9	21 56.3	11 42.4	27 14.2	5 12.4	0 16.3	21 8.4	20 22.9	23 15.0
19 Sa	28 12 36	21 2 36	12R11.9	22 49.5	12 42.9	27 48.5	5 15.6	0 15.4	21 6.2	20 21.5	23 13.7
20 Su	29 9 53	4♋27 26	12 11.2	23 39.0	13 43.7	28 22.8	5 18.9	0 14.5	21 4.1	20 20.0	23 12.4
21 M	0♋ 7 10	18 9 4	12 9.7	24 24.8	14 44.8	28 57.2	5 22.4	0 13.4	21 1.9	20 18.5	23 11.2
22 Tu	1 4 26	2♌ 4 52	12 7.5	25 6.8	15 46.2	29 31.6	5 26.0	0 12.3	20 59.7	20 17.0	23 9.9
23 W	2 1 42	16 11 26	12 4.9	25 44.9	16 47.9	0♍ 6.2	5 29.8	0 11.0	20 57.4	20 15.5	23 8.7
24 Th	2 58 57	0♍24 51	12 2.5	26 19.0	17 49.8	0 40.8	5 33.8	0 9.7	20 55.2	20 14.0	23 7.5
25 F	3 56 11	14 41 19	12 0.6	26 48.8	18 52.0	1 15.5	5 37.9	0 8.3	20 52.9	20 12.5	23 6.4
26 Sa	4 53 25	28 57 24	11 59.5	27 14.5	19 54.4	1 50.2	5 42.2	0 6.7	20 50.7	20 10.9	23 5.2
27 Su	5 50 38	13♎10 15	11D59.5	27 35.7	20 57.1	2 25.1	5 46.6	0 5.1	20 48.4	20 9.4	23 4.1
28 M	6 47 51	27 17 37	12 0.3	27 52.5	21 60.0	2 60.0	5 51.2	0 3.4	20 46.0	20 7.8	23 3.0
29 Tu	7 45 3	11♏17 44	12 1.7	28 4.8	23 3.2	3 34.9	5 56.0	0 1.6	20 43.7	20 6.2	23 2.0
30 W	8 42 15	25 9 5	12 3.0	28 12.4	24 6.5	4 10.0	6 0.9	29♒59.7	20 41.4	20 4.7	23 1.0

* giving the positions of planets daily at noon, Greenwich Mean Time

NOON EPHEMERIS: GMT*

JULY 1993

Day	☉	Noon ☽	True ☊	☿	♀	♂	♃	♄	♅	♆	♇
1 Th	9♋39 26	8♐50 17	12♐ 3.8	28♋15.4	25♉10.1	4♍45.1	6♎ 6.0	29♒57.7	20♑39.0	20♑ 3.1	22♏59.9
2 F	10 36 38	22 19 55	12R 3.5	28R 13.7	26 14.0	5 20.2	6 11.2	29R 55.7	20R 36.7	20R 1.5	22R 59.0
3 Sa	11 33 49	5♑36 41	12 1.7	28 7.5	27 18.0	5 55.5	6 16.5	29 53.5	20 34.3	19 59.9	22 58.0
4 Su	12 31 0	18 39 31	11 58.6	27 56.7	28 22.3	6 30.8	6 22.0	29 51.3	20 31.9	19 58.3	22 57.1
5 M	13 28 11	1♒27 46	11 54.1	27 41.4	29 26.7	7 6.1	6 27.7	29 49.0	20 29.6	19 56.7	22 56.2
6 Tu	14 25 22	14 1 31	11 48.9	27 22.0	0♊31.4	7 41.6	6 33.5	29 46.6	20 27.2	19 55.1	22 55.3
7 W	15 22 33	26 21 38	11 43.3	26 58.5	1 36.3	8 17.0	6 39.4	29 44.1	20 24.8	19 53.5	22 54.5
8 Th	16 19 45	8♓29 58	11 38.1	26 31.3	2 41.3	8 52.6	6 45.5	29 41.5	20 22.4	19 51.8	22 53.6
9 F	17 16 57	20 29 14	11 33.8	26 0.8	3 46.5	9 28.2	6 51.7	29 38.8	20 19.9	19 50.2	22 52.9
10 Sa	18 14 9	2♈22 59	11 30.7	25 27.5	4 52.0	10 3.9	6 58.1	29 36.1	20 17.5	19 48.6	22 52.1
11 Su	19 11 21	14 15 25	11 29.2	24 51.7	5 57.6	10 39.7	7 4.6	29 33.3	20 15.1	19 47.0	22 51.4
12 M	20 8 34	26 11 13	11D 29.1	24 14.1	7 3.3	11 15.5	7 11.2	29 30.4	20 12.7	19 45.3	22 50.7
13 Tu	21 5 48	8♉15 16	11 30.0	23 35.3	8 9.3	11 51.4	7 17.9	29 27.4	20 10.3	19 43.7	22 50.0
14 W	22 3 2	20 32 24	11 31.5	22 55.9	9 15.4	12 27.3	7 24.8	29 24.4	20 7.9	19 42.1	22 49.3
15 Th	23 0 17	3♊ 7 3	11 32.7	22 16.6	10 21.7	13 3.4	7 31.9	29 21.2	20 5.5	19 40.5	22 48.7
16 F	23 57 33	16 2 48	11R 33.0	21 38.2	11 28.1	13 39.4	7 39.0	29 18.1	20 3.0	19 38.9	22 48.1
17 Sa	24 54 49	29 21 51	11 31.8	21 1.1	12 34.7	14 15.6	7 46.3	29 14.8	20 0.6	19 37.3	22 47.6
18 Su	25 52 5	13♋ 4 37	11 28.7	20 26.3	13 41.4	14 51.8	7 53.7	29 11.5	19 58.2	19 35.6	22 47.1
19 M	26 49 22	27 9 15	11 23.7	19 54.2	14 48.3	15 28.1	8 1.3	29 8.1	19 55.8	19 34.0	22 46.6
20 Tu	27 46 40	11♌31 40	11 17.3	19 25.5	15 55.3	16 4.5	8 8.9	29 4.6	19 53.5	19 32.4	22 46.1
21 W	28 43 57	26 5 53	11 10.2	19 0.7	17 2.5	16 40.9	8 16.7	29 1.1	19 51.1	19 30.8	22 45.7
22 Th	29 41 16	10♍44 52	11 3.4	18 40.2	18 9.7	17 17.3	8 24.6	28 57.5	19 48.7	19 29.2	22 45.3
23 F	0♌38 34	25 21 42	10 57.7	18 24.6	19 17.2	17 53.9	8 32.7	28 53.8	19 46.3	19 27.6	22 45.0
24 Sa	1 35 53	9♎50 31	10 53.7	18 14.2	20 24.7	18 30.5	8 40.8	28 50.1	19 44.0	19 26.1	22 44.6
25 Su	2 33 12	24 7 12	10 51.8	18D 9.3	21 32.4	19 7.1	8 49.1	28 46.3	19 41.6	19 24.5	22 44.4
26 M	3 30 32	8♏ 9 33	10D 51.7	18 10.0	22 40.2	19 43.8	8 57.4	28 42.5	19 39.3	19 22.9	22 44.1
27 Tu	4 27 52	21 56 56	10 52.5	18 16.7	23 48.1	20 20.6	9 5.9	28 38.6	19 37.0	19 21.4	22 43.9
28 W	5 25 12	5♐29 48	10 53.5	18 29.4	24 56.2	20 57.4	9 14.5	28 34.7	19 34.7	19 19.8	22 43.7
29 Th	6 22 33	18 49 6	10R 53.4	18 48.3	26 4.3	21 34.3	9 23.2	28 30.7	19 32.4	19 18.3	22 43.5
30 F	7 19 55	1♑55 51	10 51.5	19 13.4	27 12.6	22 11.3	9 32.1	28 26.7	19 30.2	19 16.7	22 43.4
31 Sa	8 17 17	14 50 51	10 47.1	19 44.6	28 21.0	22 48.3	9 41.0	28 22.6	19 27.9	19 15.2	22 43.3

LONGITUDE

AUGUST 1993

Day	☉	Noon ☽	True ☊	☿	♀	♂	♃	♄	♅	♆	♇
1 Su	9♌14 40	27♑34 37	10♐40.1	20♋22.1	29♊29.6	23♍25.4	9♎50.0	28♒18.5	19♑25.7	19♑13.7	22♏43.2
2 M	10 12 4	10♒ 7 27	10R 30.9	21 5.7	0♋38.2	24 2.5	9 59.1	28R 14.4	19R 23.5	19R 12.2	22D 43.2
3 Tu	11 9 28	22 29 39	10 20.1	21 55.4	1 47.0	24 39.7	10 8.4	28 10.2	19 21.3	19 10.8	22 43.2
4 W	12 6 54	4♓41 48	10 8.8	22 51.1	2 55.9	25 16.9	10 17.7	28 5.9	19 19.1	19 9.3	22 43.3
5 Th	13 4 20	16 45 2	9 57.9	23 52.6	4 4.9	25 54.2	10 27.1	28 1.7	19 17.0	19 7.8	22 43.3
6 F	14 1 48	28 41 10	9 48.4	24 60.0	5 14.0	26 31.6	10 36.6	27 57.4	19 14.8	19 6.4	22 43.4
7 Sa	14 59 17	10♈32 48	9 40.9	26 12.9	6 23.2	27 9.0	10 46.3	27 53.0	19 12.7	19 5.0	22 43.6
8 Su	15 56 47	22 23 25	9 35.9	27 31.2	7 32.6	27 46.5	10 56.0	27 48.7	19 10.7	19 3.6	22 43.8
9 M	16 54 18	4♉17 12	9 33.2	28 54.7	8 42.0	28 24.0	11 5.8	27 44.3	19 8.6	19 2.2	22 44.0
10 Tu	17 51 51	16 18 57	9D 32.3	0♌23.1	9 51.6	29 1.6	11 15.7	27 39.9	19 6.6	19 0.8	22 44.2
11 W	18 49 26	28 33 50	9 32.5	1 56.2	11 1.2	29 39.3	11 25.7	27 35.4	19 4.6	18 59.4	22 44.5
12 Th	19 47 1	11♊ 7 1	9R 32.7	3 33.7	12 11.0	0♎17.0	11 35.8	27 31.0	19 2.6	18 58.1	22 44.8
13 F	20 44 39	24 3 10	9 31.9	5 15.1	13 20.9	0 54.8	11 45.9	27 26.5	19 0.7	18 56.8	22 45.1
14 Sa	21 42 17	7♋25 50	9 29.1	7 0.2	14 30.8	1 32.7	11 56.2	27 22.0	18 58.7	18 55.5	22 45.5
15 Su	22 39 57	21 16 40	9 23.9	8 48.5	15 40.9	2 10.6	12 6.5	27 17.5	18 56.9	18 54.2	22 45.9
16 M	23 37 39	5♌34 37	9 16.2	10 39.7	16 51.0	2 48.5	12 17.0	27 13.0	18 55.0	18 52.9	22 46.4
17 Tu	24 35 22	20 15 29	9 6.5	12 33.3	18 1.3	3 26.6	12 27.5	27 8.5	18 53.2	18 51.7	22 46.9
18 W	25 33 6	5♍12 3	8 55.9	14 28.9	19 11.7	4 4.7	12 38.1	27 4.0	18 51.4	18 50.4	22 47.4
19 Th	26 30 51	20 14 58	8 45.5	16 26.2	20 22.1	4 42.8	12 48.7	26 59.4	18 49.7	18 49.2	22 47.9
20 F	27 28 38	5♎14 24	8 36.6	18 24.8	21 32.6	5 21.0	12 59.5	26 54.9	18 47.9	18 48.0	22 48.5
21 Sa	28 26 26	20 1 47	8 30.0	20 24.2	22 43.2	5 59.3	13 10.3	26 50.4	18 46.2	18 46.9	22 49.1
22 Su	29 24 15	4♏30 57	8 25.9	22 24.2	23 53.9	6 37.6	13 21.2	26 45.8	18 44.6	18 45.7	22 49.8
23 M	0♍22 5	18 38 43	8 24.3	24 24.5	25 4.7	7 16.0	13 32.2	26 41.3	18 43.0	18 44.6	22 50.5
24 Tu	1 19 56	2♐24 30	8D 24.1	26 24.8	26 15.6	7 54.5	13 43.2	26 36.8	18 41.4	18 43.5	22 51.2
25 W	2 17 49	15 49 36	8R 24.2	28 24.8	27 26.6	8 33.0	13 54.4	26 32.3	18 39.9	18 42.4	22 51.9
26 Th	3 15 43	28 56 23	8 23.3	0♍24.4	28 37.6	9 11.5	14 5.5	26 27.8	18 38.4	18 41.4	22 52.7
27 F	4 13 38	11♑47 35	8 20.3	2 23.3	29 48.7	9 50.1	14 16.8	26 23.4	18 36.9	18 40.4	22 53.5
28 Sa	5 11 34	24 25 48	8 14.4	4 21.5	0♌59.9	10 28.8	14 28.1	26 18.9	18 35.5	18 39.4	22 54.4
29 Su	6 9 32	6♒53 10	8 5.5	6 18.9	2 11.2	11 7.5	14 39.5	26 14.5	18 34.1	18 38.4	22 55.3
30 M	7 7 31	19 11 20	7 53.9	8 15.2	3 22.6	11 46.3	14 50.9	26 10.1	18 32.8	18 37.5	22 56.2
31 Tu	8 5 31	1♓21 31	7 40.5	10 10.6	4 34.1	12 25.2	15 2.5	26 5.7	18 31.5	18 36.5	22 57.1

* giving the positions of planets daily at noon, Greenwich Mean Time

NOON EPHEMERIS: GMT* SEPTEMBER 1993

Day	☉	Noon ☽	True ☊	☿	♀	♂	♃	♄	♅	♆	♇
1 W	9♍ 3 34	13♓24 44	7♐26.3	12♍ 4.8	5♌45.6	13♎ 4.1	15♎14.0	26♒ 1.3	18♑30.2	18♑35.7	22♏58.1
2 Th	10 1 37	25 22 0	7R 12.6	13 57.9	6 57.2	13 43.0	15 25.7	25R 57.0	18R 29.0	18R 34.8	22 59.1
3 F	10 59 43	7♈14 42	7 0.4	15 49.9	8 9.0	14 22.0	15 37.3	25 52.7	18 27.8	18 33.9	23 0.1
4 Sa	11 57 50	19 4 43	6 50.6	17 40.6	9 20.8	15 1.1	15 49.1	25 48.4	18 26.7	18 33.1	23 1.2
5 Su	12 56 0	0♉54 38	6 43.7	19 30.2	10 32.6	15 40.2	16 0.9	25 44.2	18 25.6	18 32.3	23 2.3
6 M	13 54 11	12 47 50	6 39.5	21 18.6	11 44.6	16 19.4	16 12.8	25 40.0	18 24.6	18 31.6	23 3.4
7 Tu	14 52 24	24 48 24	6 37.7	23 5.8	12 56.6	16 58.7	16 24.7	25 35.8	18 23.6	18 30.9	23 4.6
8 W	15 50 40	7♊ 1 5	6D 37.4	24 51.8	14 8.7	17 38.0	16 36.6	25 31.7	18 22.6	18 30.2	23 5.8
9 Th	16 48 57	19 30 57	6R 37.4	26 36.7	15 20.9	18 17.4	16 48.7	25 27.7	18 21.7	18 29.5	23 7.0
10 F	17 47 16	2♋23 3	6 36.7	28 20.4	16 33.2	18 56.8	17 0.7	25 23.6	18 20.9	18 28.9	23 8.3
11 Sa	18 45 38	15 41 44	6 34.2	0♎ 3.0	17 45.5	19 36.3	17 12.9	25 19.7	18 20.1	18 28.2	23 9.6
12 Su	19 44 2	29 29 51	6 29.3	1 44.4	18 58.0	20 15.9	17 25.0	25 15.7	18 19.3	18 27.7	23 10.9
13 M	20 42 27	13♌47 48	6 21.9	3 24.7	20 10.4	20 55.5	17 37.2	25 11.9	18 18.6	18 27.1	23 12.2
14 Tu	21 40 55	28 32 40	6 12.5	5 4.0	21 23.0	21 35.2	17 49.5	25 8.1	18 17.9	18 26.6	23 13.6
15 W	22 39 25	13♍37 55	6 2.1	6 42.2	22 35.6	22 14.9	18 1.8	25 4.3	18 17.3	18 26.1	23 15.0
16 Th	23 37 56	28 53 54	5 51.9	8 19.3	23 48.3	22 54.7	18 14.1	25 0.6	18 16.7	18 25.6	23 16.4
17 F	24 36 29	14♎ 9 24	5 42.9	9 55.4	25 1.1	23 34.6	18 26.5	24 57.0	18 16.2	18 25.2	23 17.9
18 Sa	25 35 5	29 13 42	5 36.2	11 30.4	26 13.9	24 14.5	18 39.0	24 53.4	18 15.7	18 24.8	23 19.4
19 Su	26 33 42	13♏58 23	5 32.1	13 4.4	27 26.8	24 54.5	18 51.4	24 49.9	18 15.3	18 24.4	23 20.9
20 M	27 32 21	28 18 21	5 30.3	14 37.5	28 39.8	25 34.5	19 3.9	24 46.4	18 14.9	18 24.1	23 22.5
21 Tu	28 31 1	12♐11 45	5D 30.2	16 9.5	29 52.8	26 14.6	19 16.5	24 43.0	18 14.6	18 23.8	23 24.0
22 W	29 29 43	25 39 29	5R 30.7	17 40.5	1♍ 5.9	26 54.8	19 29.1	24 39.7	18 14.3	18 23.5	23 25.6
23 Th	0♎28 27	8♑44 8	5 30.5	19 10.4	2 19.0	27 35.0	19 41.7	24 36.5	18 14.1	18 23.3	23 27.2
24 F	1 27 13	21 29 14	5 28.7	20 39.4	3 32.2	28 15.3	19 54.3	24 33.3	18 13.9	18 23.1	23 28.9
25 Sa	2 26 0	3♒58 31	5 24.5	22 7.4	4 45.4	28 55.6	20 7.0	24 30.3	18 13.8	18 22.9	23 30.6
26 Su	3 24 49	16 15 29	5 17.7	23 34.4	5 58.8	29 36.0	20 19.7	24 27.2	18 13.7	18 22.8	23 32.3
27 M	4 23 39	28 23 9	5 8.5	25 0.3	7 12.1	0♏16.4	20 32.4	24 24.3	18D 13.7	18 22.7	23 34.0
28 Tu	5 22 32	10♓24 1	4 57.7	26 25.2	8 25.5	0 56.9	20 45.2	24 21.5	18 13.7	18 22.6	23 35.7
29 W	6 21 26	22 20 2	4 46.2	27 49.0	9 39.0	1 37.5	20 57.9	24 18.7	18 13.8	18 22.6	23 37.5
30 Th	7 20 22	4♈12 51	4 35.0	29 11.7	10 52.6	2 18.1	21 10.7	24 16.0	18 13.9	18D 22.6	23 39.3

LONGITUDE OCTOBER 1993

Day	☉	Noon ☽	True ☊	☿	♀	♂	♃	♄	♅	♆	♇
1 F	8♎19 21	16♈ 3 56	4♐25.1	0♏33.3	12♍ 6.2	2♏58.8	21♎23.6	24♒13.4	18♑14.1	18♑22.6	23♏41.1
2 Sa	9 18 21	27 54 54	4R 17.2	1 53.7	13 19.8	3 39.5	21 36.4	24R 10.8	18 14.3	18 22.7	23 43.0
3 Su	10 17 23	9♉47 41	4 11.6	3 13.0	14 33.5	4 20.3	21 49.3	24 8.4	18 14.6	18 22.7	23 44.8
4 M	11 16 28	21 44 41	4 8.6	4 30.9	15 47.3	5 1.2	22 2.2	24 6.1	18 14.9	18 22.9	23 46.7
5 Tu	12 15 35	3♊48 57	4D 7.7	5 47.5	17 1.1	5 42.1	22 15.1	24 3.8	18 15.3	18 23.0	23 48.6
6 W	13 14 44	16 4 6	4 8.3	7 2.7	18 15.0	6 23.1	22 28.0	24 1.6	18 15.7	18 23.2	23 50.6
7 Th	14 13 56	28 34 18	4 9.4	8 16.4	19 28.9	7 4.1	22 41.0	23 59.5	18 16.2	18 23.5	23 52.5
8 F	15 13 10	11♋23 50	4R 10.2	9 28.5	20 42.9	7 45.2	22 53.9	23 57.5	18 16.8	18 23.7	23 54.5
9 Sa	16 12 26	24 36 50	4 9.8	10 38.9	21 57.0	8 26.3	23 6.9	23 55.6	18 17.3	18 24.0	23 56.5
10 Su	17 11 44	8♌16 28	4 7.7	11 47.4	23 11.0	9 7.6	23 19.9	23 53.8	18 18.0	18 24.3	23 58.5
11 M	18 11 5	22 24 8	4 3.8	12 54.0	24 25.2	9 48.8	23 32.9	23 52.1	18 18.7	18 24.7	24 0.5
12 Tu	19 10 28	6♍58 38	3 58.3	13 58.4	25 39.4	10 30.2	23 45.9	23 50.5	18 19.4	18 25.1	24 2.6
13 W	20 9 54	21 55 29	3 51.9	15 0.4	26 53.6	11 11.6	23 59.0	23 48.9	18 20.2	18 25.5	24 4.6
14 Th	21 9 21	7♎ 7 0	3 45.4	15 59.9	28 7.9	11 53.1	24 12.0	23 47.5	18 21.0	18 26.0	24 6.7
15 F	22 8 51	22 23 7	3 39.8	16 56.6	29 22.2	12 34.6	24 25.0	23 46.2	18 21.9	18 26.5	24 8.8
16 Sa	23 8 22	7♏33 3	3 35.7	17 50.2	0♎36.5	13 16.2	24 38.1	23 44.9	18 22.9	18 27.0	24 11.0
17 Su	24 7 56	22 27 9	3 33.4	18 40.3	1 50.9	13 57.8	24 51.1	23 43.8	18 23.9	18 27.6	24 13.1
18 M	25 7 31	6♐58 20	3D 32.8	19 26.8	3 5.3	14 39.5	25 4.2	23 42.8	18 24.9	18 28.1	24 15.3
19 Tu	26 7 9	21 2 43	3 33.6	20 9.1	4 19.8	15 21.3	25 17.2	23 41.8	18 26.0	18 28.8	24 17.4
20 W	27 6 48	4♑39 24	3 35.0	20 46.9	5 34.3	16 3.1	25 30.3	23 41.0	18 27.1	18 29.4	24 19.6
21 Th	28 6 29	17 49 55	3 36.2	21 19.6	6 48.9	16 45.0	25 43.3	23 40.3	18 28.3	18 30.1	24 21.8
22 F	29 6 11	0♒37 23	3R 36.6	21 46.9	8 3.4	17 26.9	25 56.4	23 39.6	18 29.6	18 30.9	24 24.0
23 Sa	0♏ 5 56	13 5 45	3 35.7	22 8.0	9 18.0	18 8.9	26 9.4	23 39.1	18 30.9	18 31.6	24 26.3
24 Su	1 5 41	25 19 15	3 33.3	22 22.6	10 32.7	18 51.0	26 22.4	23 38.7	18 32.2	18 32.4	24 28.5
25 M	2 5 29	7♓21 59	3 29.5	22R 29.9	11 47.3	19 33.1	26 35.5	23 38.4	18 33.6	18 33.2	24 30.8
26 Tu	3 5 18	19 17 41	3 24.7	22 29.4	13 2.0	20 15.2	26 48.5	23 38.1	18 35.0	18 34.1	24 33.0
27 W	4 5 9	1♈ 9 36	3 19.4	22 20.6	14 16.8	20 57.5	27 1.5	23 38.0	18 36.5	18 35.0	24 35.3
28 Th	5 5 2	13 0 27	3 14.1	22 3.0	15 31.5	21 39.7	27 14.5	23D 38.0	18 38.0	18 35.9	24 37.6
29 F	6 4 57	24 52 31	3 9.5	21 36.1	16 46.3	22 22.1	27 27.5	23 38.1	18 39.6	18 36.8	24 39.9
30 Sa	7 4 53	6♉47 42	3 6.0	20 59.9	18 1.1	23 4.5	27 40.5	23 38.3	18 41.2	18 37.8	24 42.2
31 Su	8 4 52	18 47 46	3 3.7	20 14.5	19 16.0	23 46.9	27 53.4	23 38.6	18 42.9	18 38.8	24 44.5

* giving the positions of planets daily at noon, Greenwich Mean Time

NOON EPHEMERIS: GMT*

NOVEMBER 1993

Day	☉	Noon ☽	True ☊	☿	♀	♂	♃	♄	♅	♆	♇
1 M	9♏ 4 52	0♊54 28	3♐ 2.8	19♏20.1	20♎30.9	24♏29.4	28♎ 6.4	23♒39.0	18♑44.6	18♑39.9	24♏46.8
2 Tu	10 4 55	13 9 42	3D 3.0	18R 17.6	21 45.8	25 12.0	28 19.3	23 39.5	18 46.4	18 40.9	24 49.2
3 W	11 4 59	25 35 39	3 4.0	17 8.1	23 0.7	25 54.6	28 32.2	23 40.1	18 48.2	18 42.0	24 51.5
4 Th	12 5 6	8♋14 46	3 5.5	15 53.4	24 15.7	26 37.3	28 45.1	23 40.8	18 50.0	18 43.2	24 53.9
5 F	13 5 14	21 9 43	3 6.9	14 35.4	25 30.7	27 20.1	28 58.0	23 41.6	18 51.9	18 44.3	24 56.2
6 Sa	14 5 25	4♌23 7	3 7.8	13 16.5	26 45.7	28 2.9	29 10.8	23 42.5	18 53.9	18 45.5	24 58.6
7 Su	15 5 37	17 57 12	3R 8.0	11 59.2	28 0.8	28 45.8	29 23.7	23 43.5	18 55.9	18 46.7	25 1.0
8 M	16 5 52	1♍53 13	3 7.4	10 46.0	29 15.8	29 28.7	29 36.5	23 44.7	18 57.9	18 48.0	25 3.4
9 Tu	17 6 9	16 10 51	3 6.1	9 39.2	0♏30.9	0♐11.7	29 49.2	23 45.9	18 60.0	18 49.3	25 5.7
10 W	18 6 27	0♎47 42	3 4.5	8 40.8	1 46.1	0 54.7	0♏ 2.0	23 47.2	19 2.1	18 50.6	25 8.1
11 Th	19 6 48	15 38 59	3 2.7	7 52.4	3 1.2	1 37.8	0 14.7	23 48.6	19 4.2	18 51.9	25 10.5
12 F	20 7 11	0♏37 45	3 1.3	7 14.9	4 16.4	2 21.0	0 27.4	23 50.2	19 6.4	18 53.3	25 12.9
13 Sa	21 7 35	15 35 41	3 0.3	6 49.1	5 31.6	3 4.2	0 40.1	23 51.8	19 8.7	18 54.7	25 15.3
14 Su	22 8 1	0♐24 15	2D 59.8	6 34.9	6 46.8	3 47.5	0 52.7	23 53.5	19 10.9	18 56.1	25 17.7
15 M	23 8 29	14 55 59	2 60.0	6D 32.3	8 2.0	4 30.8	1 5.3	23 55.4	19 13.3	18 57.5	25 20.1
16 Tu	24 8 58	29 5 23	3 0.5	6 40.6	9 17.2	5 14.2	1 17.9	23 57.3	19 15.6	18 59.0	25 22.6
17 W	25 9 29	12♑49 28	3 1.2	6 59.1	10 32.5	5 57.7	1 30.4	23 59.3	19 18.0	19 0.5	25 25.0
18 Th	26 10 1	26 7 42	3 1.8	7 27.1	11 47.8	6 41.2	1 42.9	24 1.5	19 20.5	19 2.1	25 27.4
19 F	27 10 34	9♒ 1 36	3 2.4	8 3.6	13 3.0	7 24.8	1 55.3	24 3.7	19 22.9	19 3.6	25 29.8
20 Sa	28 11 8	21 34 12	3 2.7	8 47.8	14 18.3	8 8.4	2 7.7	24 6.1	19 25.5	19 5.2	25 32.2
21 Su	29 11 44	3♓49 32	3R 2.8	9 38.7	15 33.6	8 52.0	2 20.0	24 8.5	19 28.0	19 6.8	25 34.6
22 M	0♐12 20	15 52 4	3 2.7	10 35.6	16 48.9	9 35.8	2 32.3	24 11.0	19 30.6	19 8.4	25 37.0
23 Tu	1 12 58	27 46 23	3 2.7	11 37.7	18 4.3	10 19.5	2 44.6	24 13.6	19 33.2	19 10.1	25 39.4
24 W	2 13 37	9♈36 52	3D 2.6	12 44.2	19 19.6	11 3.4	2 56.8	24 16.4	19 35.9	19 11.7	25 41.8
25 Th	3 14 17	21 27 34	3 2.6	13 54.7	20 34.9	11 47.2	3 9.0	24 19.2	19 38.6	19 13.4	25 44.2
26 F	4 14 59	3♉21 58	3 2.8	15 8.5	21 50.3	12 31.2	3 21.1	24 22.1	19 41.3	19 15.2	25 46.6
27 Sa	5 15 41	15 23 0	3 2.9	16 25.2	23 5.7	13 15.2	3 33.1	24 25.1	19 44.0	19 16.9	25 48.9
28 Su	6 16 25	27 32 58	3R 3.0	17 44.3	24 21.0	13 59.2	3 45.1	24 28.2	19 46.8	19 18.7	25 51.3
29 M	7 17 10	9♊53 37	3 2.9	19 5.6	25 36.4	14 43.3	3 57.1	24 31.4	19 49.6	19 20.5	25 53.7
30 Tu	8 17 57	22 26 9	3 2.6	20 28.6	26 51.8	15 27.5	4 9.0	24 34.7	19 52.5	19 22.3	25 56.1

LONGITUDE

DECEMBER 1993

Day	☉	Noon ☽	True ☊	☿	♀	♂	♃	♄	♅	♆	♇
1 W	9♐18 44	5♋11 21	3♐ 1.9	21♏53.1	28♏ 7.2	16♐11.7	4♏20.8	24♒38.0	19♑55.4	19♑24.1	25♏58.4
2 Th	10 19 33	18 9 43	3R 1.0	23 18.8	29 22.6	16 55.9	4 32.6	24 41.5	19 58.3	19 26.0	26 0.8
3 F	11 20 23	1♌21 35	2 59.9	24 45.7	0♐38.1	17 40.2	4 44.3	24 45.1	20 1.2	19 27.8	26 3.1
4 Sa	12 21 15	14 47 8	2 58.8	26 13.5	1 53.5	18 24.6	4 56.0	24 48.7	20 4.2	19 29.7	26 5.5
5 Su	13 22 8	28 26 24	2 58.0	27 42.0	3 8.9	19 9.0	5 7.6	24 52.4	20 7.2	19 31.6	26 7.8
6 M	14 23 2	12♍19 9	2D 57.7	29 11.2	4 24.4	19 53.5	5 19.1	24 56.2	20 10.3	19 33.6	26 10.1
7 Tu	15 23 57	26 24 43	2 58.0	0♐41.0	5 39.8	20 38.0	5 30.6	25 0.1	20 13.3	19 35.5	26 12.4
8 W	16 24 54	10♎41 37	2 58.8	2 11.2	6 55.3	21 22.6	5 41.9	25 4.1	20 16.4	19 37.5	26 14.7
9 Th	17 25 52	25 7 27	2 59.9	3 41.8	8 10.8	22 7.2	5 53.3	25 8.2	20 19.5	19 39.4	26 17.0
10 F	18 26 51	9♏38 36	3 1.0	5 12.8	9 26.3	22 51.9	6 4.5	25 12.4	20 22.6	19 41.4	26 19.3
11 Sa	19 27 51	24 10 23	3R 1.7	6 44.0	10 41.8	23 36.7	6 15.7	25 16.6	20 25.8	19 43.5	26 21.5
12 Su	20 28 53	8♐37 20	3 1.7	8 15.6	11 57.3	24 21.4	6 26.8	25 20.9	20 29.0	19 45.5	26 23.8
13 M	21 29 55	22 53 49	3 0.7	9 47.3	13 12.8	25 6.3	6 37.8	25 25.3	20 32.2	19 47.5	26 26.0
14 Tu	22 30 58	6♑54 42	2 58.7	11 19.3	14 28.3	25 51.2	6 48.7	25 29.8	20 35.4	19 49.6	26 28.3
15 W	23 32 2	20 36 4	2 55.9	12 51.4	15 43.8	26 36.1	6 59.6	25 34.4	20 38.7	19 51.7	26 30.5
16 Th	24 33 6	3♒55 39	2 52.6	14 23.8	16 59.3	27 21.1	7 10.4	25 39.0	20 41.9	19 53.8	26 32.7
17 F	25 34 11	16 53 2	2 49.3	15 56.3	18 14.8	28 6.1	7 21.1	25 43.7	20 45.2	19 55.9	26 34.8
18 Sa	26 35 16	29 29 33	2 46.4	17 29.0	19 30.3	28 51.2	7 31.7	25 48.5	20 48.5	19 58.0	26 37.0
19 Su	27 36 21	11♓48 2	2 44.4	19 1.8	20 45.8	29 36.4	7 42.2	25 53.4	20 51.9	20 0.1	26 39.2
20 M	28 37 26	23 52 22	2D 43.4	20 34.8	22 1.3	0♑21.5	7 52.6	25 58.3	20 55.2	20 2.3	26 41.3
21 Tu	29 38 32	5♈47 10	2 43.5	22 8.0	23 16.8	1 6.7	8 2.9	26 3.3	20 58.6	20 4.4	26 43.4
22 W	0♑39 38	17 37 23	2 44.7	23 41.4	24 32.3	1 52.0	8 13.2	26 8.4	21 2.0	20 6.6	26 45.5
23 Th	1 40 45	29 28 3	2 46.4	25 14.9	25 47.8	2 37.3	8 23.3	26 13.6	21 5.4	20 8.8	26 47.6
24 F	2 41 51	11♉23 54	2 48.2	26 48.7	27 3.4	3 22.7	8 33.4	26 18.8	21 8.8	20 11.0	26 49.6
25 Sa	3 42 58	23 29 13	2 49.6	28 22.7	28 18.9	4 8.1	8 43.3	26 24.1	21 12.2	20 13.2	26 51.7
26 Su	4 44 5	5♊47 34	2R 49.9	29 56.9	29 34.4	4 53.5	8 53.2	26 29.4	21 15.6	20 15.4	26 53.7
27 M	5 45 12	18 21 30	2 48.7	1♑31.4	0♑49.9	5 39.0	9 2.9	26 34.9	21 19.1	20 17.6	26 55.7
28 Tu	6 46 19	1♋12 27	2 45.8	3 6.1	2 5.4	6 24.5	9 12.6	26 40.3	21 22.6	20 19.8	26 57.7
29 W	7 47 26	14 20 37	2 41.2	4 41.1	3 20.9	7 10.1	9 22.1	26 45.9	21 26.0	20 22.0	26 59.6
30 Th	8 48 34	27 44 56	2 35.5	6 16.4	4 36.4	7 55.7	9 31.6	26 51.5	21 29.5	20 24.3	27 1.5
31 F	9 49 42	11♌23 17	2 29.1	7 52.0	5 51.8	8 41.4	9 40.9	26 57.2	21 33.0	20 26.5	27 3.5

* giving the positions of planets daily at noon, Greenwich Mean Time

Why Asteroids?

The discovery of the first asteroids points to the rebirth of the Goddess in women's spirituality. Traditional astrology uses only 2 planets to symbolize female archetypes: Moon as mother and Venus as mate. As a result, astrological language has tried to fit all other women's experiences into male-defined archetypes.

When a heavenly body is prominent in the sky at the time of a person's birth, the mythological story of the god or goddess who shares the same name as the planet or asteroid becomes a major theme in that individual's life.

Ceres, the Great Mother, provides a model to understand the causes of eating disorders, co-dependency, child sexual abuse and incest, the wounded child, dysfunctional families, the trauma of separation between parents and children due to the breakup of families and challenges of single-parenting. Ceres also encompasses the ancient knowledge of conscious dying and the psychological death and rebirth transformation process.

Pallas Athena, Goddess of Wisdom, refers to the dilemma of professional women who sacrifice relationship or children for career, sexism in the professional world, the wounds from the father-daughter interaction, androgeny, and taking responsibility for creating our reality. Pallas also provides insights into the causes of disease due to breakdown of the auto-immune system, and is a key to understanding learning disorders.

Vesta, the Temple Priestess, illuminates the need to reintegrate spiritual and sexual energies, focus on self-healing, find our vocation or meaningful work, and develop a deeper relationship with our own soul. Vesta symbolizes the importance of following a spiritual path to heal addictions and offers a clue to the spread of sexually transmitted diseases.

Juno, the Goddess of Marriage, speaks to the redefinition of meaningful relationships, lesbian and gay couples, changing sexual roles, and the plight of powerless and battered women. Juno's story provides a foundation to understand the issues of projection, love addiction, dependency, domination, obsession, jealousy, betrayal, trust and power themes in relationships.

In addition, the asteroids help clarify and enhance the horoscope's existing astrological themes. It is not unusual for the asteroids to group around the major points of focus in the chart and complete major Aspect patterns.

© *Demetra George 1991, author of* Asteroid Goddesses

1993 Asteroid Ephemeris

Reprinted with permission from Astro-Computing Services

1993	Ceres 1	Pallas 2	Juno 3	Vesta 4	Sappho 80	Amor 1221	Pandora 55	Icarus 1566
JAN 1	20≈28.1	25♍31.0	05♌R37.8	27✓26.9	05✓10.2	25♉R45.8	19♍R38.0	25✓54.7
11	24 07.5	29 07.4	03 28.0	02♑49.1	09 30.1	24 13.7	18 07.6	04♑00.7
21	27 52.6	02♎43.4	01 53.6	08 09.0	13 47.0	23D50.2	16 08.1	10 56.4
31	01♓42.2	06 17.9	01 07.5	13 25.7	17 59.8	24 32.7	13 51.7	17 00.5
FEB 10	05 35.1	09 49.7	01D13.1	18 38.3	22 07.0	26 14.5	11 33.9	22 25.6
20	09 30.1	13 17.9	02 07.0	23 46.0	26 07.5	28 48.2	09 29.3	27 20.3
MAR 2	13 26.4	16 41.2	03 42.9	28 47.8	29 59.3	02♊07.5	07 50.6	01≈49.1
12	17 22.8	19 58.5	05 54.3	03≈42.7	03♑40.4	06 06.8	06 45.7	05 54.8
22	21 18.7	23 08.5	08 34.6	08 29.6	07 08.4	10 41.8	06 17.4	09 38.9
APR 1	25 13.1	26 09.8	11 38.2	13 07.1	10 20.2	15 49.6	06D25.8	13 00.9
11	29 04.9	29 00.8	14 59.8	17 33.6	13 12.4	21 27.8	07 08.2	15 59.7
21	02♈53.6	01♏39.9	18 35.6	21 47.6	15 40.7	27 35.0	08 20.7	18 32.9
MAY 1	06 38.0	04 04.9	22 22.8	25 46.7	17 39.9	04♋10.7	09 59.5	20 36.1
11	10 17.0	06 13.6	26 18.4	29 28.5	19 04.5	11 13.9	12 00.6	22 03.8
21	13 49.7	08 03.6	00♍20.4	02♓50.1	19 48.7	18 44.8	14 20.5	22 47.9
31	17 14.7	09 31.6	04 27.3	05 47.7	19R47.0	26 43.2	16 56.2	22R37.1
JUN 10	20 30.5	10 34.8	08 37.7	08 17.5	18 57.2	05♌08.3	19 45.1	21 18.3
20	23 35.5	11 09.8	12 50.5	10 14.5	17 20.9	13 59.6	22 44.9	18 35.6
30	26 27.5	11R13.3	17 04.8	11 33.5	15 07.6	23 15.7	25 53.8	14 15.7
JUL 10	29 04.4	10 43.1	21 19.8	12 10.0	12 35.2	02♍54.0	29 10.0	08 17.6
20	01♉23.3	09 38.2	25 35.1	12R00.0	10 06.2	12 51.3	02♎32.4	01 03.0
30	03 20.9	08 00.0	29 49.9	11 02.6	08 04.1	23 02.8	05 59.8	23♑23.2
AUG 9	04 53.8	05 53.8	04♎03.7	09 22.0	06 46.5	03♎22.3	09 30.9	16 20.9
19	05 58.2	03 27.9	08 16.1	07 08.4	06D22.4	13 42.9	13 04.9	10 42.0
29	06 30.0	00 54.3	12 26.5	04 38.9	06 54.4	23 57.3	16 41.0	06 44.9
SEP 8	06R26.2	28♎26.5	16 34.5	02 13.9	08 19.2	03♏58.2	20 18.3	04 24.8
18	05 45.2	26 16.5	20 39.4	00 12.1	10 31.6	13 40.0	23 55.9	03 27.6
28	04 27.8	24 34.1	24 40.7	28≈48.0	13 25.6	22 58.6	27 33.1	03D38.5
OCT 8	02 39.5	23 25.0	28 37.8	28 08.9	16 54.9	01✓51.6	01♏08.8	04 44.1
18	00 29.7	22 51.3	02♏29.5	28D15.9	20 54.3	10 18.4	04 42.3	06 34.4
28	28♈12.3	22D52.6	06 15.1	29 06.8	25 19.2	18 19.7	08 12.4	09 02.3
NOV 7	26 02.7	23 26.4	09 53.6	00♓36.7	00≈54.5	25 56.7	11 37.9	12 02.4
17	24 14.8	24 29.7	13 23.7	02 40.5	05 09.6	03♑11.6	14 57.6	15 32.0
27	22 59.3	25 59.1	16 43.7	05 13.2	10 29.0	10 06.1	18 09.8	19 29.6
DEC 7	21 21.6	27 51.1	19 52.0	08 09.7	16 00.7	16 42.1	21 13.0	23 55.2
17	22D23.2	00♏02.5	22 46.6	11 26.2	21 42.8	23 01.8	24 05.1	28 50.6
27	22 02.9	02 30.5	25 24.8	14 59.3	27 33.2	29 06.6	26 43.7	04≈17.6
JAN 6	24♈16.9	05♏12.5	27 44.3	18 45.7	03♓30.1	04≈57.8	29 06.5	10 14.2

1993	Psyche 16	Eros 433	Lilith 1181	Toro 1685	Diana 78	Hidalgo 944	Urania 30	Chiron 2060
JAN 1	12♏29.5	01✓55.2	24♎43.9	19✓22.0	05♓49.4	03♏02.2	13≈33.7	22♏R58.9
11	15 07.4	09 01.1	26 58.1	25 04.9	09 04.1	03 56.4	18 35.9	22 28.4
21	17 31.0	15 52.5	28 48.1	00♑55.9	12 30.1	04 34.1	23 43.9	21 50.5
31	19 37.5	22 28.8	00♏10.2	06 56.3	16 05.8	04 53.7	28 56.9	21 07.4
FEB 10	21 23.9	28 49.9	01 00.9	13 07.8	19 49.6	04R54.0	04♓13.9	20 21.7
20	22 47.4	04♑55.6	01R17.0	19 33.0	23 40.3	04 34.6	09 34.4	19 36.1
MAR 2	23 44.4	10 45.1	00 56.3	26 14.6	27 36.6	03 55.7	14 57.6	18 53.1
12	24 12.2	16 17.7	29♎59.1	03≈15.9	01♈35.5	02 58.7	20 22.7	18 15.3
22	24R08.6	21 32.5	28 23.8	10 41.6	05 42.2	01 45.9	25 49.4	17 44.9
APR 1	23 32.4	26 27.6	26 30.8	18 36.4	09 49.9	00 21.0	01♈17.0	17 23.3
11	22 25.1	01≈01.1	24 17.7	27 06.1	13 59.8	28♎48.9	06 44.8	17 11.7
21	20 50.9	05 10.4	22 02.1	06♓17.1	18 11.3	27 14.6	12 12.5	17D10.7
MAY 1	18 57.0	08 51.4	19 57.4	16 14.8	22 23.8	25 43.5	17 39.4	17 20.5
11	16 54.0	11 59.7	18 15.0	27 03.3	26 36.4	24 20.6	23 04.9	17 40.8
21	14 53.4	14 29.0	17 02.2	08♈43.4	00♉48.9	23 09.7	28 28.6	18 11.2
31	13 06.6	16 11.3	16 23.1	21 09.7	05 00.4	22 13.8	03♉49.7	18 50.9
JUN 10	11 42.7	16 58.1	16D18.0	04♉10.9	10 02.1	21 34.5	09 07.6	19 39.1
20	10 47.6	16R39.8	16 45.2	17 31.4	13 17.6	21 12.4	14 21.5	20 34.8
30	10 24.9	15 09.0	17 42.0	00♊53.5	17 21.6	21D07.4	19 30.5	21 37.2
JUL 10	10D33.1	12 26.1	19 04.9	14 02.2	21 21.1	21 18.6	24 33.5	22 45.1
20	11 24.2	08 42.8	20 50.5	26 46.0	25 15.0	21 44.8	29 29.5	23 57.6
30	12 19.8	04 27.6	22 55.9	08♋56.0	29 01.6	22 24.6	04♊16.8	25 13.6
AUG 9	13 52.5	00 19.6	25 18.0	20 26.8	02♊39.0	23 16.5	08 53.8	26 32.2
19	15 47.5	26♑54.3	27 54.5	01♌15.7	06 05.1	24 18.9	13 18.5	27 52.2
29	18 02.1	24 36.1	00♏43.2	11 22.4	09 16.7	25 30.3	17 28.1	29 12.8
SEP 8	20 33.6	23 32.4	03 42.1	20 48.7	12 10.6	26 49.2	21 19.8	00✓32.7
18	23 19.0	23D40.0	06 49.8	29 38.0	14 42.5	28 11.4	24 49.6	01 51.0
28	26 19.0	24 51.2	10 04.7	07♍53.3	16 47.3	29 43.7	27 52.9	03 06.5
OCT 8	29 29.0	26 56.0	13 25.3	15 38.2	19 19.6	01♏22.6	00♋24.7	04 18.0
18	02✓48.6	29 45.7	16 51.3	22 55.8	19 13.2	02 51.3	02 18.5	05 24.6
28	06 16.1	03≈13.5	20 22.5	29 48.4	19 04.9	04 26.4	03 15.6	06 24.8
NOV 7	09 29.0	07 13.0	23 52.8	06♎18.4	18 44.9	06 01.1	03R47.8	07 17.6
17	13 30.4	11 39.9	27 26.9	12 27.4	17 20.9	07 33.5	03 14.1	08 01.9
27	17 14.9	16 30.9	01✓01.3	18 16.0	15 19.0	09 02.3	01 49.0	08 36.5
DEC 7	21 02.8	21 42.9	04 35.5	23 45.2	12 55.3	10 26.1	29♊24.7	09 00.7
17	24 53.4	27 14.3	08 08.4	28 54.8	10 31.5	11 43.5	27 10.0	09 13.8
27	28 45.3	03♓03.6	11 38.8	03♏43.8	08 30.6	12 52.7	24 37.5	09R15.4
JAN 6	02♑37.8	09 09.5	15 05.5	08 11.4	07♊10.0	13 52.5	22 27.5	09♍05.6

Acknowledgments

I am grateful as always for the a'mazing web of wemoon creating this book. First of all, I want to thank the contributors whose by-lines follow. We see the beauty in our aliveness through your wonderfilled art. Your creativity blesses our days—may your work be blessed as well!

For the first time ever, we have had an inner circle of wemoon living and working together on the land, producing the **We'Moon** from beginning to end...and being paid for it! Thank you all for being here for this in such a spirited way: Oriana (apprentice "Wemoonager") for your many talents as busyness organizer, editor, graphic / altar artist, and office priestess; Beth Free♀ for your artful work as "Contributor Hag" in correspondence, in rituals, and paste-up; Lava for being there in the beginning with your magic and international outreach efforts; and Marna for joining us just in time to finish up, as fledgling MacQueen artist and group work visionary. We also appreciate the help of others on and around We'Moon Healing Ground for proof-reading, providing occasional meals, bodywork, and cheer, and for generally bearing with us: Lori, Kelly, Kate, Diana, Bean, and Solstice.

"We'Moon Weaving Circles" are the way we process the art and writings when they are first gathered in—by passing it through the hands of many wemoon on different wemoon lands in Oregon for initial feedback. Special thanks for the invaluable work of the We'Moon Weavers this year: Bethroot and Madrone at Fly Away Home; Julie at Rainbow's End; Ursula, Marti, Beatrice, Rhea Earth, Luna Moon, and Felice Ana at OWL; and Ila Suzanne (also a fine editor), Judith Burros, Catherine Sicilian for being the We'Moon Weaver Midwives, pulling together the work of the other circles.

Final production work was done on our own Sophia (a MacDyke Classic, named after the Greek Goddess of Wisdom) and Chodron (laser printer: "lamp of the dharma" in Tibetan). Many thanks, Francis, for coming all the way from S. Oregon to pass on your Pagemaker teachings so patiently and your technological experience with previous **We'Moon**'s. Thanks, Jemma Crae, for your continuously recycling loan; to Kali Rose and Sandra Lea LeBel in Atlanta, Georgia for your careful proofreading of astrological data, and to Jeri Baumgardner of In Her Image Gallery (Portland, OR) for her help in networking wemoon artists. I would also like to acknowledge Astro-Computing Services (San Diego, CA) for providing all the astrological data.

Credit / Copyrights / Contacts

Contributor By-lines

Aimee Mattila (Eugene, Oregon): My artwork is a ceremony in itself. It happens when I am able to set aside the time and space to center and focus and allow the creative juices to flow. Art is a way of life for me, it is a part of my spirit.

A. Kimberlin Blackburn (Kapaa, Hawaii): A multi-media artist, I am blessed with dreams and visions and the place to bring them forth. I share in the Goddesses and would love to do so with all of you.

Amikaeyla Gaston (Washington D.C.): I am of Native American & African descent. I am a jazz singer, artist, pianist & potter. I hope to bring these gifts to the medical arena, along with my feminist spirit, taking me to the streets and international dominions.

Angela Von Lintel Lobitz (Baton Rouge, Louisiana): Artist and mother of 4 grown children. When I first started working with mandalas a friend described them as a "Celebration of Subtleties". Celebration of the awesome creation that is the natural world we live in is what I strive to express through art.

Angelina Marino (Portland, Oregon): is a Northwest artist and poet, currently represented by Radiance Gallery in Portland.

Ann Hendahl Owen (Waddy, Kentucky): is an artist/professor/art therapist. Making art helps me understand myself and my world. Working intuitively from dreams is scary but evolves into my deeper truths.

Anne Kirby McCarthy (New Paltz, New York): I am a poet and womanist. I believe in trees, the Great Spirit, and the power to heal Our Mother and her children. Mitukuyasin.

Annie Ocean (Rainbow's Other End, Oregon): is a photographer, radical lesbian naturalist living 13 years on lesbian land. She finds her spirituality in the wilds and in recovery. She is a blue witch who does political and spiritual work focusing on the environment and breaking silence about incest.

Antiga (Minneapolis, Minnesota): is a feminist witch, dyke, writer, singer, artist, workshop facilitator and outrageous womoon. She is currently working on a book, "Y in I ching", and singing at every possible opportunity.

B. Lynn DiBiase (Eugene, Oregon): I am an artist and writer. I create artwork for fat womyn, and the people who care about them, to instill a positive fat image on our collective psyches. I also hope to empower fat women who relate to these drawings so they realize their own vitality and true Goddess selves.

Bev Severn (Denman Island, B.C., Canada): mother, potter, artist, teacher. I am lucky enough to live on a beautiful island where I work and celebrate life with friends and my daughter, Alana. My sculptural and decorative claywork reflects my love of nature and creativity of the Goddess within.

Billie Miracle (Grants Pass, Oregon): is a pastel and graphic artist living on women's land for 16 years. She is a founder of Woman Share and is a community/ cultural worker.

Boa Snake♀ (OWL Farm, Oregon): I am a Pisces, living on land, going through my midlife transformation/healing. Living as simply and separatistly as possible, slowing down, learning to listen. I would also very much like to hear from other wemoon who have had/are having visions/dreams.

Boudykke (Minneapolis, Minnesota): is an irreverent fat dyke of Italian, French and English descent. Her hobbies are trying to outsmart the patriarchy and looking toward a lesbian future.

Brooke Medicine Eagle (Ovando, Montana): Through the renewal of ancient ritual forms for creating a beautiful path upon the Earth, Brooke Medicine Eagle, Earthkeeper, teacher and healer, dedicates herself to bringing Spirit alive on Mother Earth.

Carina King (London, U.K.): is a dancer and artist.

Carolyn Hillyer (Devon, U.K.): is an artist living on the edge of the wild and mist-veiled mystery of Dartmoor (S.W. England) and honouring in paint the faces of the Divine Mother that she finds there. She dances with the Sacred Corn and mothers Leaf and Cedar (to be).

Carolyn McTaggart (Kamloops, B.C., Canada): I'm an artist, costume maker, story-teller and tree planter. I'm a student of Hygiea College, relearning womancraft and loving it. My roots are in the earth deep, so I'm at home anywhere.

Chesca Potter (London, U.K.): is an artist inspired by the sacred Goddess of this land.

Colette Gardiner (Eugene, Oregon): is a witch of European American descent. Her family has lived in Oregon for 7 generations. She currently offers classes, workshops and apprenticeships on herb lore. She enjoys cats, gardens and dancing.

Colleen Mary McGuire (Boston, Massachusetts): Painter and teacher. A moment to thank my mother, Mary Esther, who gave me strength, determination and the love of self and others.

Debby Earthdaughter (Tucson, Arizona): I'm 30, german/unknown heritage, living on SSI with chemical sensitivity. I'm part of Saguaroland—for dykes with disabilities and allies—part of SHE Land Trust, PO Box 5285 Tucson, AZ 85703.

Deborah Koff-Chapin (Langley, Washington): has been developing and teaching the process of touch drawing since it was revealed to her in ecstatic play in 1974. She is the co-author of "At the Pool of Wonder" (Bear & Co.) and her work is available at In Her Image Gallery in Portland, Oregon.

Diana Rose Hartmann (Calabasas, California): I am 32 years of age (May 17, 1960, taurus sun, scorpio rising, aquarius moon). I enjoy cats, the earth, talk to trees, like the smell of horses, rituals.

Durga T. Bernhard (Shandaken, New York): is a painter and printmaker whose intensive studies of the art and lore of tribal cultures have led to the creation of numerous goddess and fertility images. She lives with her husband and two children in the Catskill Mountains.

Elizabeth Dietz Gauerke (Chicago, Illinois): A Chippewa elder, astrologist and activist for Native American rights. Her self-published manuscript, *The Medicine Road,* and "Grandmother Moon", an address she gave to the American Astrological Association, provide a valuable lunar perspective to astrology. (See page 23.)

Emerald Goldman (Portland, Oregon): I was born in Los Angeles in 1946 and studied Art at UCLA. The first time I visited Oregon one cold, rainy December, I fell in love with her. I've been living here for 16 years now. I've shown my work in Oregon, Washington and California. I live with my cat, Samson and my dog, Delilah.

Erin DeLuna (Calgary, Canada): a charming yet devastatingly fierce pseudo-communistic, radical-feministic environmentalist and witch with latent lesbian tendencies, whose work is continuously inspired by whatever the Goddess gives her. Blessed be.

Eva-Gesine Wegner (Frankfurt, Germany): a sculptress in Western Germany who believes in the energies of old holy places and is involved in creating new ones in German cities for today.

Ffiona Morgan (Forestville, California): is a wild Welsh witchwomon who loves the Goddess and the earth with a passion. She is the author of the "Daughters of the Moon" Tarot Deck and Book, and "Wild Witches Don't Get the Blues".

Genece Klein (Vancouver, Washington): is an illustrator and graphic designer who has shown her artwork at regional galleries.

Gentle Doe (Santa Fe, New Mexico): author of two books: "Heart Medicine" and "Soft Glow Hard Wax". She is co-creator of the Original Deepening Cards, published by Rose Press. Her lifework draws from shamanism, 12-step Recovery, Native American Indian spirituality and Tibetan Buddhism.

Gretchen Lawlor (Langley, Washington): old astrologer, works the oracle only occasionally these days. Busy with the plant spirits of my Northwest island, finding ways to help us all mutate gracefully and quickly enough to enjoy the future.

Hana Amazon (OWL Farm, Oregon): I'm a creative, working class, white, dyke, separatist witch. I'm a lover, healing from incest and patriarchy.

Helen Free♀ (Oakland, California): I'm 29, Jewish, a lesbian leo fire child, earth lover, truth speaker, singer-songwriter, artist. I'm dedicated to challenging oppressions and creating safe, supportive space with other radical witches.

Ila Suzanne (Portland, Oregon): I am celebrating my 50th year. White, lesbian, witch, poet. My work has appeared in "We Are Everywhere" (Crossing Press); "Awakening" (Wordweavers); and other lesbian publications. I have written two chapbooks: "They Gathered In Groves" & "There Will Be Signs".

Jan Larsson (Cannon Beach, Oregon): I am a teacher who has chosen to step outside the classroom of four walls into the classroom of the Universe. I live by the ocean and she teaches me. In sending you these offerings, I am honoring my Higher Purpose.

Jane Lowe (AKA Morgan of Art) (Berkeley, California): is a Dianic priestess initiated by Z. Budapest in 1990. She lives with her cat, Girleen, in her love temple. She is quoted as saying: "Next time I'm working in steel".

Jane Reichhold (Gualala, California): It is very clear to me that these are not <u>my</u> haiku but that they are given to me in moments of my openness to something beyond myself. To the Giver of these states of Grace, I am very thankful.

Janine Canan (traveling): is the editor of "She Rises Like the Sun", and the author of 6 books of poetry, most recently "Her Magnificent Body" and "New & Selected Poems". After practicing psychiatry for 15 years in Berkeley she is now journeying in Asia and Europe at work on 2 new books.

Jeanne Morrison Colin (Falls Church, Virginia): an artist, a mother, a custodian of the earth, & a Taurus Monkey. I have no home, yet live as many places as possible; I conform to nothing; my job is to disrupt and change and awaken, my purpose is to show that there are other ways to be.

Jennifer Brice (London, U.K.): is a poet whose collection "Working in the Cracks Between" was published by Aquila in 1990. She is now working on a new series of poems based on flight (both literal and metaphorical). She often visits the U.S. as a lecturer and workshop leader.

Jill Smith (Isle of Lewis, U.K.): I live alone with my son. I draw my vision of spirit of place and stones. I write poems of what I experience. The place I live called me to her and will not let me go. If you want to know what booklets I have for sale, write to me at Tigh-A-Ghlinne, Gravir, Isle of Lewis, U.K.

Jo Ann George (Angoon, Alaska): She was introduced to the Tlingit Indian lifestyle through her marriage and subsequent life in a Tlingit village. She combines Tlingit-style designs and a representational style of art to illustrate mystical aspects of the culture and its involvement with the natural world.

Joys Dancer (Birch Lake, Saskatchewan, Canada): lives in a forest on the shores of a small lake, mothering, gardening, en-visioning healing, balance, harmony and peace within self, family, community & planet; expressing vision through music, environmental work and prayer.

Judith Burros (Portland, Oregon): artist, quilter, photographer, survivor, searcher, finder of memories...

Judy Springer (Ontario, Canada): is a very fishy pisces with a soft spot for chickens on the road and lesbians everywhere.

Julie Hopp (Roseburg, Oregon): is a Jewish dyke living on Lesbian Land in southern Oregon. I work in the woods and illustrate astrological birth charts.

Kelly Blue Sky (We'Moon Healing Ground, Oregon): Warrior maid, carpenter, lover of winds against my face, lesbians, mama earth and all her beauty-filled creatures. Love the land!

Kit Cameron (San Francisco, California): I use my art as a way to reach the space outside of time. Making the work is a private act of devotion; sharing it with the wider world makes it a public act as well.

Kitt Redwing (Canada): is an artist of life, traveling where it takes her.

Kiwani (Whaletown, British Columbia): having moved to an island on the west coast, I visualize lesbian communities on land bases with temple gardens dedicated to the continued healing of Gaia.

Kris Russel (Sacramento, California): Woman-identified writer/poet, searcher and recovering soul from the northwoods trying to find peace amidst the patriarchy.

L. Jordan Peck (formerly Lynn) (Ovando, Montana): I am having my first painting show in my new home state in May 1992. Transformation continues; I give thanks for the circle of strong women that mirrors the strength I need to go on.

Laura Anderson (Cameroon, Africa): singer and songwriter, I love playing guitar. I've taught English and French in Cameroon with the Peace Corps and lived close to the land in communal groups. Committed to peace projects, working on relieving hunger and building on women's land.

Laurie Burke York (Albion, California): is a visual artist whose work is included in the anthology "She Who Was Lost Is Remembered" (Seal Press). She is a grant recipient of the Druid Heights Artists Retreat in New Mexico.

Lava (Germany): life-artist dancing between continents and worlds, discovering myself within my lesbian visions.

Leaf (California and Oregon): Jewish, lesbian separatist committed to being a vegan, loves to create lesbian art and music, build, cook and live in the country.

Lillian Pitt (Portland, Oregon): a native woman of Warm Springs/Yakima heritage, her clay masks, using Raku and Anagama methods of firing, are embellished with feathers, beads and shells, resulting in a unique style without precedence in Northwest Coast art.

Lorain Karol (Oregon City, Oregon): is a Priestess who serves the Lady. Editor of Rosehips Journal of the Elder Faith.

Lori Moon Nicolosi (Hainesport, New Jersey): With her work in clay she explores her feelings about being a wombin, with all the glory and strength it has to offer. In a society that doesn't always validate this, she tries to evoke strength and courage for her sisters to be proud of who we are.

Louise Chambers (Denver, Colorado): I am a Lesbian Feminist Radical WItch. I am beginning to use my words and visual images to create female space, female culture.

Marcia Cohee (Laguna Beach, California): I live with my husband Pat and daughter Devin. We host the Laguna Poets, a weekly reading series. My books: "Sexual Terrain" and Laguna Canyon Was Once A River".

Mari Jackson (Nacogdoches, Texas): a witch whose art is her Craft.

Mari Susan Selby (Santa Fe, New Mexico): My poetry is a gift of my healing offered for others and the planet. I love women, the earth and laughter, in any particular order. I am a bodyworker/therapist by trade, and an astrologer/healer witch in my heart and soul.

Marj Johnston (Cooloorta, Republic of Ireland): I'm 40, living on top of two fairy forts and experiencing a life of death and rebirth. I'm a tarot reader, gardener and herbalist living in constant contact with fairies and earth spirits.

Maryanne Powers (Miami, Florida): Lesbian artist and co-nurturer of "Something Special", a lesbian venture offering vegetarian meals and wimmin-only space in the midst of Miami's madness.

Megan Wilson (Eugene, Oregon): I am a radical eco-feminist/anarchist artist and writer. My work deals with my experiences and visions of celebrating life from a pagan perspective.

Melane Lohmann (Ovando, Montana): I'm a poet, earthkeeper, cook and horse-woman. In my work as assistant to Brooke Medicine Eagle, I practice these convictions: that to heal ourselves is to heal our Mother Earth, as we are in fact one with Her body; and that in honoring Spirit, we honor the connection between all living things.

Melissa Harris (New York, New York): My work consists of life size, psychological, theatrical portraits painted in oil. I like painting mystics, tarot readers, etc., where I depict the transformation of energy within the individual during the sessions and between myself and the sitter.

Minerva (Kaitaia, New Zealand): artist, astrologer, dreamer living with wonderful challenging lesbian wimmin's land. Everlearning the loving, healing way of the Goddess: trust and surrender to my own path.

Mirtha Vega (Santa Fe, New Mexico): is a mother, healer, priestess, writer, lover of life. My poems and writings are part of a book I am preparing, "Regaining Our Power: Awakening the Warrioress Within". Blessed be ! P.S. I am a scorpio!

Monica Sjoo (Bristol, England): an artist, writer and pioneer in women's art, politics and spirituality in Great Britain and Scandinavia. She is co-author of The Great Cosmic Mother with Barbara Mor (Harper & Row, 1988), and has recently finished *New Age or Armageddon* (Women's Press, 1992) about New Age patriarchy.

Musawa (We'Moon Healing Ground, Oregon): I live in a little house I built in the woods by a creek among green ferns, firs, cedars, and tender leafy sprouts and spirits, with 7 other wemoon on the land. I have been part of creating community on wemoon lands for over 20 years now, and it still feels like we are just learning the basics of how to live in a healing way with ourselves, each other, and the earth. I also do body/mind/spirit therapy in Portland, Oregon and carry on with **We'Moon.**

Nancy Blair (North Brunswick, New Jersey): (our front cover artist) is an artist and writer, owner of Star River Productions, Inc., The Great Goddess Collection Gift Catalog. She is living, dreaming and playing in the rhythms of the Goddess!

Nancy Rutherford (Greenville, New York): I am a woman birthing my aliveness and hopefully supporting others to do the same for the glory of the earth. Artist/Priestess living and healing with dear friends and cats and the wild animals and loving spirits that grace us with their presence on holy land.

Ni Aodagain (OWL Farm, Oregon): living deeply, prayerfully with other we'moon to create womon space based on love of the Mother and each other—hard work, but the only work there is for me at this great changing time for wimmin and the Earth.

Nicola Beechsquirrel (Dyfed, Cymru, South Wales, U.K.): mother, poet, artist, activist in Pagans Against Nukes and the Pagan Parenting Network News.

Oriol Dancer (Birch Lake, Saskatchewan, Canada): I feed the birds, listen to their songs and find myself singing along. I paint beauty all around me; I am grateful for the gift of each sunrise and sunset. I dance with the moon learning about cycles/time, spinning and weaving harmonious moments.

Oriana (We'Moon Healing Ground, Oregon): is a radical, separatist, dyke witch living with her cat, Vesta, and creating magic flower gardens and groves in which to celebrate a Goddessfull life in the cuntree with her sisters. She is an artist and writer, currently creating a witchywomon novel and allowing the songs to pour out of her.

Pat Siddall (Eugene, Oregon): I am a sea creature but live in the valley by necessity. I am a bodyworker who leans toward the healing of the spirit and emotions as a way to access healing for physical pain. I have a daughter, a wonderful lover, Robin, and an entourage of cats, rat & gerbil.

Patricia Levey (San Francisco, California): I have been using self-portrait photography as a means to self-discovery, empowerment and healing for 12 years. My most recent body of work, "Awakening the Spirit", was created while on retreat in New Mexico.

Patricia Zukas (Silver Spring, Maryland): Printmaking is a relatively new medium for me; I experienced it in school at the Maryland Institute, College of Art, where I received my MFA. I have a son, Christopher, who I am co-parenting with another woman.

Rosemary Sheola (Wendell, Massachusetts):She divides her time between freelance writing and working at a women's health care clinic, organizing seasonal rituals and community events and single parenting. Her interests include poetry, music, herbology, traveling and storytelling.

Ruth Zachary (Lansing, Michigan): My work is characterized by symbolic imagery and includes references from mythology. I have always been drawn to create images about women. My backgrounds in literature and sociology, as well as art, all come together in my work.

Sami Gray (Earth): Lesbian, rural dweller, involved with arts, yoga, Buddhism, gardening & nature studies.

Sandra Pastorius (aka Laughing Giraffe) (Santa Cruz, California): I am currently working with the Sanctuary of Gaia and the Holy Hemp Sisters creating community, rituals and gatherings dedicated to the Earth as Sacred Being/Sacred Place.

Saya Wolf (Espanola, New Mexico): is an ecstatic dancer; lover of the wind, rain, sun-drenched stone; friend of wild creatures; author; spiritual companion, Bone sister and priestess of the Goddess.

Sequoia (Eugene, Oregon): Living, learning, vegetarian earth-loving potter. Ritual cups, rattles, candle holders, functional pottery & custom designs. For info, send SASE to: PO Box 1585 Eugene, OR 97401.

Sheila Broun (Leeds, U.K.): I am an artist and maskmaker who has been working with the Goddess & Festivals of the Year for some time—creating rituals and artwork. I also teach art and design and am writing my dissertation on Menstruation—exploring the links between culture and identity.

Shemaya Mountain Laurel (Shutesbury, Massachusetts): woods-dyke learning to travel on wheels, living non-toxic and scent-free, disability the teacher...still flying.

Shereon (Cumbria, U.K.): this painting, a dream image, is one of many paintings of nature spirits done shortly after the unbelievably beautiful birth of my second son, Holly, on the morning of Winter Solstice.

Shoshana Rothaizer (Flushing, New York): is a native New Yorker who connects Mother Nature's rhythms and spirits both in city and country. She hopes that her photography serves as a bridge between people of different lifestyles. Brochure of her postcards available: 147-44 69th Rd., Flushing, NY 11367.

Starr Goode (Santa Monica, California): is a writer and a video producer. She is also a witch in the coven of Nemesis and a founding member of Goddess Project LA.

Sudie Rakusin (Hillsborough, North Carolina): is an Aries with 5 other planets in Fire, an artist living with 3 dog companions in the woods surrounded by ever expanding gardens, dealing on a personal daily level with the major transformation going on in the universe.

Sue Silvermarie: is a descendant of Irish, Norwegian and Italian witches who works with old women as a Poetry Therapist and has just finished her 3rd book of poetry, *Dance Your Slow Way Home*.

Sunlight (Comptche, California): I live in a valley surrounded by hills of redwood trees where it is easy to hear the Goddess within. A few years ago she gave me a book called BEING that helps women listen to her voice.

Susanne Hare (Tofino, British Columbia): I live on an island, fighting for what's left of this ancient forest. I am a mother of 4 children. I'm 46 years old and do graphics and large sculptures.

Suzanne Benton (Ridgefield, Connecticut): makes metal masks, monoprints and is also a performance artist. Her multi-cultural images draw upon diverse archetypal imagery, myth, history, literature and legend. In September 1992 she began a year long world journey of creating art and sharing.

V.S. Sekhmet (Menlo Park, California): is an artist and a writer.

Vicki Ledray Grabicki (Issaquah, Washington): I paint ancient memories, ones that we all share. I paint animals and my love and concern for their future. I bring their spirits into this world so they can speak to us of our connectedness with all things.

Willow Elliot (Redmond, Oregon): is a bodyworker, community networker and caretaker of sacred land and ancient forests, as well as a yurt dweller. For retreats to sacred land, write: 6250 N.W. Atkinson, Redmond, OR 97756.

Zana (Tucson, Arizona): I'm 45, Jewish, living in land-trust community with other disability-activist lesbians. "Herb Womon", a collection of my poetry & art is available for $7. (print or tape) from me: 12101 W. Calle Madero, Tucson, AZ 85743.

Front Cover Notes
(*Nile River Goddess*, sculpture by Nancy Blair)

Ancient Egyptians experienced the Nile River's continually changing flow as a benificent blessing of Divine Mother Nature. The river, whose moving waters pulsed in time with the rhythms of the changing moon, brought life to all Her peoples, all Her creatures. This bird or serpent-headed Goddess symbolizes the Creatrix, Source of Eternally Renewing Life. She lifts Her wings/arms joyfully clebrating powers of transformation and intuition and the strength of all women. The original sculpture is approximately 5,000 years old.

Look for Nancy's new divination amulets, *With Goddess As My Guide*, forthcoming from Wingbow Press in April 1992.

Back Cover Notes
(*Moontime* by Deborah Koff-Chapin)

Prints are avilable of *Moontime* and other works by Deborah Koff-Chapin at In Her Image Gallery, 3208 S.E. Hawthorne, Portland, Oregon 97214 USA, (503) 231-3726.

A Special Note About Our Book

In our ongoing efforts to provide the highest quality product, we are using some brand new technology with our binding this year. **We'Moon '93** will still lay flat for ease of writing—you can even fold it back entirely. We have tested this new system and feel it offers more durability and a better appearance. We welcome your comments about living with your **We'Moon.**

WE WELCOME YOUR GRAPHIC ART AND BRIEF WRITINGS FOR:

The ongoing theme for the decade of the Gaia Nineties:
WE'MOON, EARTH, and ALL OUR RELATIONS

WE'MOON '94: CYCLES

celebrating cycles, circles, spiral dance; seasons, elements, natural rhythms, moon phases, day & night; we'moon cycles, life transitions, rites of passage.
Due Date: December 21, 1992

WE'MOON '95: SURVIVORS/ THE HEALER WITHIN

healing from abuse, survival strategies, the spirit in exile, inner healer, natural child, embodying our truth, paths to recovery, the Wise Wemoon Tradition.
Due Date: May 1, 1993

Please note: The theme for **WE'MOON '94** has been changed to include aspects of "Elemental Power" that are an overflow from this year's theme. **WE'MOON '94: CYCLES** will be a celebration of the first 13 years of **We'Moon**. We invite We'Moon artists, writers, and readers over the years to contribute to the **CYCLES** issue. It will also include "oldies but goodies" from previous **We'Moons**. That means the **SURVIVORS** issue will now be moved up to the We'Moon '95. Please note: we are collecting materials now for both the **We'Moon '94 and '95**.

SPECIFICATIONS:

1) <u>artwork</u>: black and white (or high contrast) photos, drawings, quality photocopies; camera-ready (prints not negatives)

2) <u>writings</u>: short poems, stories, songs, rituals, journal entries, quotes, descriptions (300 words maximum)

© Louise Chambers 1990

Please enclose with your work:

• A BRIEF BY-LINE (one or two lines at most; will edit to fit)
• A SIGNED RELEASE (granting Mother Tongue Ink permission to publish)
• 2 S.A.S.E.'s (self-addressed, stamped envelopes)

SHARE YOUR WORK WITH WE'MOON OF MANY CULTURES
Contributors receive international recognition and free **We'Moons**. Feature artists, writers & cover artists are paid. We'moon support wemoon.